CHEMICAL INDUSTRY, UPHELD BY PURE SCIENCE, SUSTAINS THE
PRODUCTION OF MAN'S NECESSITIES

MAN
IN A
CHEMICAL WORLD

THE SERVICE OF CHEMICAL INDUSTRY

By

A. Cressy Morrison

CHARLES SCRIBNER'S SONS · NEW YORK
CHARLES SCRIBNER'S SONS · LTD · LONDON
1937

Acknowledgment

The preparation of this review of the great contribution of chemical industry to every human being was an outgrowth of the very remarkable celebration of the three hundredth anniversary of the birth of chemical industry in the United States. The Executive Committee of the American Chemical Industries Tercentenary appreciated the possibilities and usefulness of such a volume. The responsibility for its production, under the auspices of the Committee, was placed upon the author and the task was gladly accepted as an opportunity to be of service to the chemical industry which, for almost a lifetime, has contributed so much to his livelihood and happiness.

In the preparation of this volume many have helped. It is a privilege to acknowledge, with deep appreciation, the vision and suggestions of Arthur W. Hixson, Chairman of the Executive Committee, whose splendid leadership brought about the unparalleled gathering of all those connected with chemistry and the chemical industry in New York City in April, 1935. The constant and generous assistance which has been accorded by D. H. Killeffer, whose well-known ability as a writer and whose breadth of technical information, covering completely the chemical industry, have been essential in bringing together the mass of facts condensed in this small volume, cannot be spoken of too highly. The expert guidance of Lois W. Woodford has been called upon to clarify the language and check the inevitable errors. The illustrations were made by Leon Soderston, and the index by D. D. Berolzheimer. Space will not permit individual acknowledgment of great help from many in the chemical industry who checked the preliminary manuscript.   A. C. M.

300 Madison Ave., New York.
April, 1937.

Contents

Foreword

THIS BOOK is intended to be educational, from the cultural as well as the utilitarian points of view. Its object is to impress the man in the street with the fact that the chemical industries of the United States render a service that touches practically every activity in which he engages. In fact, it is the main purpose of the book to awaken him to the realization that he is utterly dependent upon these industries not only for the necessities and luxuries of life, but also for his very existence.

In his early youth he learned that "From dust thou art and unto dust shalt thou return," the poet's way of telling him that he is the very essence of chemistry. During the last twenty years, he has been told in eloquent volumes that chemistry is the key to modern material civilization, and the hope of the future. He has not been told, however, that he is able to enjoy the blessings of chemical science, largely in the form of high standards of living, because for generations industries requiring the investment of hundreds of millions of dollars and the employment of thousands of skilled and technically trained men have had to be established and operated. He is not aware of the fact that these industries are mighty pillars of support for the nation's whole industrial mechanism and means of defense supplying products that are basic for practically every other industry. Too often he has heard that the chief business of American chemical industries is to furnish products for the creation of human misery and the destruction of human life. This is a false and unmerited indictment of one of the nation's best servants and of the work of thousands of her finest scientists.

In 1935 the American Chemical Society celebrated the three hundredth anniversary of the founding of chemical industries in America with the largest chemical meeting ever held. It pointed with pride to a record of achievement which few other American industries can match and of which every citizen of the United States should be proud. The New York Section of this great scientific society, through its Tercentenary Committee, which planned and carried out the great anniversary celebration, included in its continuing program the publication of a book, to be written in language that any intelligent person could understand, that would interpret the vital service of the chemical industries in everyday life in terms of human experience.

This is the book. It is a proud record of the accomplishments of man in the rôle of creator. It was not intended that it should be a profound contribution to the literature of theoretical or applied chemistry. However, for the person who will take the trouble to read it, there will be a full measure of enjoyment and a broadening general knowledge of his relationship to material things. He will have a better understanding of the part that applied chemical science has had in raising the plane of his living to a higher level than that enjoyed by any previous generation. The authorship has been in good hands. Seldom does one find a writer who can present the accomplishments of a great industry with such enthusiasm and charm. This book is the clear sparkling distillate of the wide experience gained during a lifetime of devoted service to an industry that has helped mightily to strengthen the pulse of the nation from its very beginning.

For the student who is considering a career in science, and especially for those who have the heavy responsibility of vocational guidance, this book should be a real help. Finally, to the great army of chemists, chemical engineers, industrialists and officials of both state and nation to whom the responsibility of stewardship has been entrusted, the fine record of service to citizen and nation set forth in these pages should be a constant challenge and inspiration. ARTHUR W. HIXSON,
Columbia University.

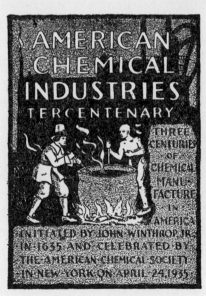

MAN
IN A
CHEMICAL WORLD

1.

Nature Points the Way

NATURE is the great chemist. All the processes of Nature involve chemical changes which vitally affect you and me; indeed are the processes of our very existence. The chemist observes and studies Nature's methods to discover means by which he can emulate or change her products, create new substances or better adapt natural materials to the uses of man. The chemical industry, utilizing the results of this research, endeavors to anticipate and supply man's developing needs for material things, thus contributing mightily to the advance of civilization.

Everywhere and at all times in their daily life people are brought in touch with and influenced by the prod-

I

ucts of chemistry, for their health, convenience, pleasure, knowledge and happiness. Indeed, every human being is a chemical factory within himself, and mysterious chemical changes which still puzzle the best informed specialist take place within the living body. Small wonder that the intelligent public wants to know more about the interesting subject of the application of the forces of chemistry to the economic well-being of our country.

The idea that Nature's products are flawless and that they fail in service because of human adulterations is one of the most popular fallacies of our time. It is almost exceptional to find a natural raw material that is the best for the use to which man puts it; as a rule Nature's material is merely the best to be had, or the cheapest. Frequently it contains deleterious impurities and lack of uniformity is always troublesome. It is at this point that applied chemistry has been of incalculable importance.

A survey of the commonplaces of the earth itself, those things which every one takes for granted, reveals chemical inter-relationships wonderful beyond measure. Let us accept for a moment the theory that the earth was formed by the passage of some star near enough to the sun to cause an enormous tidal wave which drew out into space a mass of heated gases which, cooling, changed into a liquid and finally into the familiar solid state. The ninety-two different elements which the mass contained combined to form the crust of the earth and the water of the oceans and left free the gases of the air. The crust of the earth is called the lithosphere, the waters the hydrosphere, and the air the

atmosphere. Little is known about the composition of
the center of the earth. Man's deepest drilling has
stopped short of three miles. The wracking of the surface of the earth by earthquake, volcanic eruptions,
erosion of running water, and the building up and tear-
ing down of mountains accounts for bringing to the
surface rocks which may have come from a depth of
fifty or seventy miles. Beyond this, we are unable to go
with certainty.

Here and there in the crust of the earth were left
little remnants of the original elements, now cooled and
solidified. Among these we find gold, silver, copper,
platinum and the diamond. The great mass of the
earth's crust, however, is composed of chemically combined substances. Nature brought the atoms of elements together and they acted as they do now in the

chemical laboratory. Oxygen joined hydrogen and supplied the waters of the earth. Oxygen joined iron and gave iron ore. Silicon joined oxygen and the result was silica or quartz rock, flint, the sands of the beach, and the beautiful iridescent opal. These various oxides, which consist of oxygen combined with other elements, form the greater part of the crust of the earth. Innumerable combinations were similarly formed from the elemental substances which were originally drawn from the sun. But these naturally occurring combinations are only a small fraction of the total number of possible compounds chemists today are engaged in making and studying.

Molecules and their constituent atoms are so infinitesimally small that picturing them is extremely difficult. If a single drop of water were magnified to the size of the earth, each molecule contained in it would be no larger than a baseball. Each of these molecules of water is made up of at least three atoms, two of hydrogen and one of oxygen, held together by their mutual attractions, but within each atom are large empty spaces. Even the molecules themselves are not closely packed together like oranges in a box, but rather they resemble a swarm of bees. They are in constant motion in straight lines and collide frequently with each other, bounding off again as do billiard balls.

In air and other gases, the molecules rush about at a speed which at ordinary temperatures is of the order of a thousand feet per second. The hotter they are the faster they go, and of course the reverse is also true. Enough cooling converts a gas into a liquid whose molecules are much more closely packed, and ultimately to a solid whose molecules are relatively close together, but still far apart.

In this respect, what is true of one kind of matter is true of all kinds. Even so solid an object as a steel hammer is made up primarily of a great deal of vacant space thinly populated by the tiny particles we call "electrons" dashing like planets about a nucleus at perfectly stupendous speeds. Thus, a blow on the head with a hammer is actually delivered by a material made up almost entirely of empty space in which a swarm of electrons and nuclei fly around like gnats in the summer sun! It is one of Nature's jokes, and a ghastly one, that so gauzy a thing as a hammer could hurt so much.

It has been found that the deeper we bore into the earth the hotter it becomes, and it is thus calculated that the interior of the earth must be at a temperature which would cause the center to be a molten mass. This mass may, however, have the characteristics of a solid like steel because of the terrific pressure of tons per square inch to which it is subjected.

By means of an instrument called the spectroscope, astronomers and physicists have discovered that the elements which compose the sun and the stars are almost exactly the same as those that compose the earth. But the excessive heat of the sun and stars prevents these elements from combining, so that in the sun and stars, iron exists as iron; silicon as silicon; aluminum as aluminum. Similarly, the oxygen cannot combine with the hydrogen to form water, nor with iron to form iron ore, nor can other atoms combine, and so there are no combined substances in the stars. But here on earth, as the process of cooling took place, the flying atoms slowed down so that when they came into contact with different atoms for which they had affinity, various combinations instantly took place to form the many natural substances with which we are familiar. For illustration, atoms of oxygen and hydrogen cannot combine above 4000°, but when they meet at a lower temperature, they grasp each other and hold on for dear life in a form which is called water vapor.

Now, if this water vapor is cooled sufficiently, it condenses to form droplets, which gather into clouds of white steam. These natural clouds further condense into rain which pours upon the earth as water. The boiling point of water is 212° Fahrenheit at atmospheric pressure. The molecules of this combined hydrogen and oxygen, now in the liquid state, still have considerable motion, but if the temperature falls below 32° Fahrenheit, which we call the freezing point, the molecules are slowed down until the water turns to a solid condition and ice is formed.

All of the combinations which form the crust of the earth have gone through a similar process, except those residues which have not yet combined and which are found in comparatively small quantities. These processes of combination—which take place at varying reaction speeds from very high temperatures down through what is called ordinary temperature, the normal condition, to absolute zero, which means there is no heat at all—can be reversed. By the application of heat or by introducing other forces for causing substances to

6

react on each other, or by the use of electricity, these
chemical combinations can be broken up and many of
the constituents restored to their elemental conditions.
This is the fundamental task of the chemist. More remarkable, however, and of far-reaching significance to
the human race, the chemist has learned to recombine
atoms in such manner as to obtain materials more useful, more available, less costly or more suitable than are
found conveniently in Nature. He can produce many
new substances which exist nowhere in Nature.

The twenty-six letters of the alphabet can be combined into hundreds of thousands of words, each with
a different meaning. Change one letter in a word and
it becomes something utterly new and different. What
then are the potentialities before the chemist with
ninety-two elements at his command? By changing the
combinations of the elements, the chemist can give the
world a multitude of new and useful substances. The
chemical manufacturer, having seen demonstrated by
research the possibility of making these changes, sets up
equipment to produce the new substance economically
and in the required quantity, thus serving, as no other
industry can, the expanding needs of man. This brings
the processes of chemistry right home to every individual.

Nature, however, still holds the key to an astounding
secret. Man is yet unable to say how the first living
cell was formed and to explain the mystery of life which
animates these cells. The cells themselves are composed of molecules of entirely familiar matter, and the
chemist, by careful analysis, is able to tell of what ele-

7

ments they are composed and how much of each is present. But the "why" still eludes him.

This is no place for philosophy as to the origin of life. We can only stand in reverential awe. Let it suffice to assume that the original single living cell, presumably made up of numbers of molecules, grew to a certain magnitude and then divided, as such cells do, into two cells, each endowed with the capacity to utilize the substances of the earth, elemental and combined, for food, for growth, and for reproduction. One class of these divided cells seems to have decided to remain in place and let food come to it, and the other class decided to go out and seek food. As time went on, those who decided to utilize what food came to them became vegetation, and those who went out to seek nourishment became animal life. As the policy adopted by these cells developed, they grew farther and farther apart. One perhaps became seaweed and the other a fish; one became the forest and the other a man; but it was found that they were still mutually dependent upon each other. Those who wait for their nutriment utilize chiefly those elements and combinations we call inorganic substances, while animate creatures are dependent upon the organic substances produced by vegetation.

Vegetable life uses the combination of carbon and oxygen known as carbon dioxide and, with the aid of the light from the sun, breaks up this compound, using the carbon and letting the oxygen free; while animals breathe the oxygen of the air, combine it with carbon which they have taken into their systems as vegetation, and release the carbon dioxide which plants need.

A tree is a good illustration. The roots, which are made up of cells, push farther and farther from the trunk seeking water and chemicals which are to be found in the earth. Its branches spread wider and wider, or climb towards heaven to top the forest, in order to get sunshine and the necessary carbon from the air to make the trunk. Only a small part of the tree itself comes out of the earth. Its great weight and majestic spread are due largely to the carbon which has been taken out of the air. By a process known as photosynthesis, it has formed complex carbohydrates, among them cellulose, which, together with plant juices containing various mineral substances taken from the earth, make up the fibrous structure of a tree. When wood is burned, the greater part goes up the chimney as carbon dioxide and water vapor. The oxygen of the air combines in the heat of the flame with the carbon and the hydrogen in the log, thus restoring carbon dioxide and water vapor to the atmosphere. The residue or ash contains all the minerals which have been taken out of the earth. Here, indeed, is a chemical industry, for a tree has been produced from such simple substances as carbon dioxide (the gas of the soda fountain), water and a small quantity of mineral matter. Nature thus manufactures the forest, the grass, the fruit and the flowers. The fruit of one plant may be a peach, of another a cantaloupe, and of still another a potato and all may be growing in the same soil. Thinking of all the perfumes of the garden, all the coloring of the flowers, together with the immense variety of food for all the animals and all the insects and the fishes of the sea, can we not say that in plant life alone, Nature's chemical industry is beyond human comprehension?

Now, let us turn to animal life. Its amazing variety is greater than that of the plants, for there are myriads of living creatures, those that fly, those that walk or crawl upon the earth, those that burrow beneath it, and those that swim in the waters, and these all live upon the products of vegetable life. Even those animals which have no other source of food than other animals are merely getting the chemical elements which originally came into animal life through vegetation. Here is chemistry in such an amazing complexity that it is still beyond the ability of any chemist to explain all its mysteries. The food taken into the stomach must be chemically transformed to be available for maintaining life, then transmitted to various parts of the body to supply sustenance and repair the continual waste which goes on. Bones must be built up, muscles restored, the eyes supplied with their requirements. Enamel for the teeth must be produced and horny textures maintained. The tissues of the brain and the nerves in every part of the body must be supplied with nutriment and kept in such delicate sensitivity that the slightest touch is immediately telegraphed to the brain, and thence relayed to bring some other part of the body into action. Our bodies must be kept warm literally by burning carbon compounds at low temperatures with the oxygen we breathe, a process which supplies the carbon dioxide needed by plants. It has been said that every tissue of the body must be replaced every seven years. Whether this statement is literally true as to time or in detail is unimportant, for renewal and repair are constant.

All living things follow the basic law which brought life from a single cell or later from the combination of two cells. Cells divide today, as they did millions of years ago, and so increase and grow until the embryo is formed, nourished and assembled to become a man, an elephant or a grasshopper. Some subtle chemistry tells them where to go and how to act. Some form in proper shape the lens of the eye, another group the ear. Some go to the right and some to the left and stop at the right place so that one's ears are opposite each other, both eyes in front, and so on, *ad infinitum*. It is apparent that some great force not clearly grasped is at work here. Do atoms and molecules think? Man is animated chemistry, living chemically in a chemical world that is a tiny speck in a chemical universe, but is that all?

To quote Alexis Carrel: "An organ (of a living body) builds itself by techniques very foreign to the human mind. It is not made of extraneous material, like a house. Neither is it a cellular construction, a mere assemblage of cells. It is, of course, composed of cells, as a house is of bricks. But it is born from a cell, as if the house originated from one brick, a magic brick that would set about manufacturing other bricks. Those bricks, without waiting for the architect's drawings or the coming of the bricklayers, would assemble themselves and form the walls. They would also metamorphose into window-panes, roofing-slates, coal for heating, and water for the kitchen and the bathroom. An organ develops by means such as those attributed to fairies in the tales told to children in bygone times. It is engendered by cells which, to all appearance, have a knowledge of the future edifice, and synthesize from substances contained in blood plasma the building material and even the workers."*

When one realizes that Nature has brought forth the body of man, and in that body placed a mechanism which can interpret Nature; that man is beginning to reach out and reproduce natural substances and synthesize others which have never existed in nature; that man can reason and classify, divide and analyze, and generalize conceptions which reach to the very heavens; then one realizes that in the chemistry of Nature is epitomized the foundation of all progress. Chemistry covers all the conditions of life and is intimately connected with every act of every human being. From the standpoint of the layman, the subject is intensely interesting, dramatic, and abounding with surprises. Knowledge of the simple facts of chemistry engenders an understanding sense of obligation to the patient scientists who have revealed its practical applications and to the foresighted builders of plants and processes capable of rendering these unparalleled gifts available for the use of man.

While discovering the secrets of his own complex mechanism, the chemist has charted the progress of civilization. New products unfolded by his skill are destined in a short span to become new necessities. The chemical industry is the agency equipped to supply these material requirements.

* *Man the Unknown*, by Alexis Carrel; Harper & Brothers, New York.

2.

Chemistry in Overalls

ALTHOUGH Nature, the great chemist, has provided man with the prototypes and methods by which he has attempted, with considerable success, to conquer his environment, her motives and objectives have seldom been man's. The beautiful silks with which man bedecks himself and his womankind, the sweet odors of flowers, the warmth of woolen clothing, the metals from which tools are fashioned, and countless other blessings of Nature were created for far different purposes than those to which man has put them. It is beyond us to fathom the great plan of Creation in which we play at most a very minor role, but obviously the value of natural products to us is wholly fortuitous.

13

The pleasing sheen of silk fabrics is a mere accident quite unrelated to the primary purpose for which Nature taught the silkworm to spin its filaments. The protection of the young silkworm during its development into a butterfly is too far from personal adornment for one to believe that silk clothing was intended as a gift of Nature to man. Similarly, there is grave doubt of Nature's special consideration for man in giving odors and colors to flowers, warm and water-resistant wool coats to sheep, and a bountiful supply of metals and ores to the earth to form its structure. Nature's countless blessings are too well fitted for their original purposes and too poorly adapted for man's use for one seriously to entertain the thought that no improvement can be made in them.

Man's inquisitive nature has goaded him on to look deeply into these matters and to study the causes which produce effects useful to him. The result has been the development of that most practical of sciences, chemistry, which deals with the materials of the universe and their changes. Not content to occupy the post of a mere observer of Nature's intricate occupations, man has developed his own methods, patterned after natural prototypes but often going far beyond them, of converting available materials into forms more useful than any Nature provides. An important outcome of this independence of thought and action has been the development of a vast industry based on the chemical transformation of common raw materials into highly intricate and desirable substances.

Upon these foundations, the chemical industry in

the United States has grown from its founding here at the time of the earliest white settlements.

In this important industry many men have part. Each of them, from the controllers of the destinies of vast corporations to the humblest workmen, is equally essential to the production of the necessities and comforts of men. Indeed, upon all of them and upon each of them depend the livelihoods of multitudes of others. In subsequent chapters the peculiar utility of products of chemical manufacture in many industries will be discussed and it will be found that whole armies of workers in apparently unrelated fields depend for their jobs on the fact that chemical industry continues to supply necessary materials. Indeed, it is not an overstatement to say that practically every one of this country's forty-odd million employed persons owes his job to chemical industry! This responsibility of workers in chemical industry is reflected in many ways, not the least important of which is their greater earning power as compared with corresponding workers in other industries. The creation of the National Recovery Administration in 1933 brought with it a demand for a minimum wage of forty cents per hour and a maximum working week of forty-eight hours as an almost ideal condition for workers. It found, however, that already this favorable condition was below the standards in force in chemical industry. Contrast this with the fact that chemical industry's workers are now being paid more than sixty cents per hour for less than forty hours' work and the recognition accorded labor by this industry becomes evident. In addition to the mere matter of monetary rewards, important though it is, workers in chemical industry have a pardonable pride that they materialize the abstruse concepts of the world's scientists and make them readily available to all the people; that they are peculiarly the real miracle workers of today; and that they, by making jobs for millions of other workers, are contributing mightily to the life of the world.

To illustrate the extraordinary way in which this industry functions and to show its important contribution to human welfare, consider the way in which it has assumed the role of the humble silkworm. Nature gave the silkworm the power to spin a cocoon of slender filaments around itself for protection during the period of gradual change from worm to moth. For this purpose the filaments must be strong, warm, and proof against the weather. The cylindrical shape, and the smooth and shiny surface of the filament seem the merest accident. However, these appealed to man as a desirable set of properties for his clothing. Hence, the poor worm is robbed of his protective coating to provide the fibers for a man's apparel. So long as nothing better was to be had, this source of splendid raiment was satisfactory. Chemists have learned ways to make strong, smooth, cylindrical fibers in factories by digesting cellulose, the building material of vegetation, with various chemical products and squirting the resulting sirup through tiny orifices into other chemicals which harden it into solid, extremely slender filaments. In a sense man's process duplicates that which mulberry leaves undergo in the digestive system of the silkworm. There is, however, this important difference: the silk-

THE CHEMICAL INDUSTRY

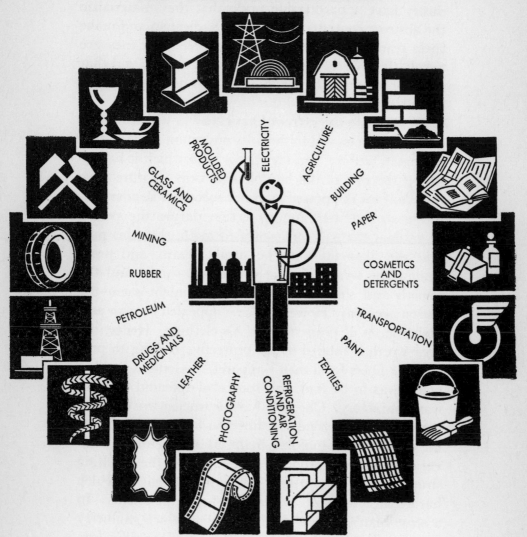

MOULDED PRODUCTS
ELECTRICITY
AGRICULTURE
BUILDING
PAPER
GLASS AND CERAMICS
MINING
RUBBER
COSMETICS AND DETERGENTS
PETROLEUM
TRANSPORTATION
DRUGS AND MEDICINALS
PAINT
LEATHER
TEXTILES
PHOTOGRAPHY
REFRIGERATION AND AIR CONDITIONING

CENTER OF MODERN LIFE

worm is bent upon producing needed protection for itself at the most important period during its life cycle, while man's manufacturing has no other objective than meeting certain of his needs. This difference is fundamental in all operations of chemical industry for, while Nature may utilize the best possible methods of attaining her objectives, these are not designed to help in man's effort to control and master his world.

Carrying this idea farther, one finds a most striking variety of useful results which have been secured by making "silk" under complete control without reference to the comfort or happiness of an oriental worm. Cellulose is one of the most plentiful of Nature's products from which has been fashioned the structures of all plants from the highest and noblest trees to the lowliest weeds. Unlike mulberry leaves, it is available from sources widely scattered over the earth. A universal raw material thus replaces a very limited one. When fibers are made by man, their dimensions, strength and other characteristics can be varied at will and not left to the instinct of the silkworm. This has allowed us to make filaments of precisely the kinds we wish and the chemical industry produces them in the widest variety. Dimensions from a greater fineness than that of silk itself to great glistening sheets which wrap our packages; from strength comparable even to steel to an elasticity approaching that of rubber; with resistance as desired to moisture, fire, sunlight and other agencies which tend to injure or destroy them; and with ability to take up the myriad hues of modern dyes which make the finished goods attractive. The role

of chemists in finding the way to accomplish these transformations, and of chemical industry in performing
them, is no less wonderful because the magic of the
changes involved is reduced to terms of long, tedious
searching and huge expenditures of labor and money.

It is obvious in this, as in all its operations, that the
chemical industry is closely knit with the sciences of
chemistry, physics and biology from which it draws its
basic thought. Nor is it strange that this close relationship with the earnest workers of science should give
to the industry most directly utilizing their findings a
character compounded of large measures of the altru-
ism and earnest sincerity of scientific thought occa-
sionally lacking in industrial organizations.

As this discussion proceeds, it will be apparent that,
although individuals buy and use few actual products
of chemical manufacture directly, few articles of our
daily lives could be made without the use somewhere in
their fabrication of chemical products which are essential in imparting to them their useful characters. It
will become apparent that chemical industry functions
particularly in converting natural products into more
useful forms which will undergo further elaboration
in other industries before being supplied directly to the
people. In a very real sense, the chemical industry con-
stitutes a vital service of supply to all industry in its
transformations of plentiful and relatively unservice-
able raw materials into hosts of industrial essentials.

Relatively few fundamental raw materials are universally used and their production and elaboration are
the basis of all chemical manufacture. Statistical data

regarding these universally used products furnish dependable indices to the economic state of industry as a whole and to the advances of civilization over longer periods, because of the complex interweaving of chemical production with all the activities of our daily lives.

It will be well to become acquainted with these basic materials and their immediate elaboration. Among the hosts of natural products made useful by chemical change, the volumes daily consumed of water, air, sulfur, salt, lime, coal, and the constituents of petroleum and natural gas are by far greater than any of the others. Not only is each of these materials the basis of an industry of its own, but the products of each are elaborated into innumerable secondary products of essential value to other industries.

Water's place in industrial operations is universally vital. In chemical industry it is made to yield the hydrogen and oxygen of which it is formed to serve as necessary tools in other chemical transformations. Wherever one turns in the world of materials water is always essential and with a few notable exceptions must always be taken into consideration. Indeed, one of the first cares of the builder of an industrial plant, whatever may be its nature (and particularly a chemical manufacturing plant), is to locate it conveniently with respect to a supply of pure water. Where this is not to be had for one reason or another, products of chemical industry are utilized to purify available supplies to make them useful. Specifically, water is the great source of hydrogen for such essential chemical productions as the synthesis of ammonia, the hardening of vegetable fats to improve them for many purposes, and for other important uses. This is, of course, quite aside from its all-important role in the development of power and its service as the well-nigh universal solvent. Natural waters, containing varieties of valuable impurities, are also important sources of many of the chemical elements invaluable in many ways. Natural brines yield salt, magnesium, chlorine, bromine (also now recovered from the waters of the sea), iodine and other elements contributing as we shall see later to our health, our speedy transportation by land and by air, and scores of other activities.

Air has traditionally supplied the oxygen necessary to the combustion of our fuels. It has latterly become the basis of several branches of chemical industry each of which contributes to our advancing civilization. Its oxygen when separated and concentrated fortifies the air breathed by injured lungs and relieves them of part of their burden. It also makes possible our modern methods of fabricating metals. The nitrogen separated from air by various means is an important raw material of fertilizers, explosives, dyes, and modern nitro-cellulose plastics, and lacquers after it has been forced to enter chemical union with other elements. The residue of the air after these valuable constituents have been separated consists of a mixture of a number of important gases, having wide usefulness in modern lighting which they have both improved and cheapened significantly.

Sulfur, produced in immense quantities from deep-lying deposits on our Gulf Coast, is the prime raw ma-

terial for the manufacture of sulfuric acid and sulfuric
acid is the most widely used member of the large family
of acids. The production of sulfuric acid varies in
precise ratio with the index of general business and
where differences occur between the various other business barometers and the sulfuric acid curve, the latter
is probably nearest to the truth. Its changes follow
business changes closely because it is produced as consumed and does not ordinarily lend itself to storage.

Salt (sodium chloride), itself an essential material,
yields the fundamental alkalies and chlorine, products
equally useful and equally general in their importance
to all branches of our industrial system. Unlike sulfuric
acid, the alkalies lend themselves rather easily to storage and hence it is not uncommon that an alkali manufacturer should accumulate stocks from time to time.
In this way, alkali production introduces another phase
into the index of business conditions, that of confidence
in future trends, which is not included in the sulfuric
acid curve. By combining the two curves, those of
sulfuric acid and of soda production, their value as an
indicator of business activity is materially enhanced.
Alkalies are more largely used in the textile industry,
for instance, and sulfuric acid finds its largest market
in fertilizers.

Black, disagreeable coal-tar, made during the conversion of coal to coke and manufactured gas, becomes,
in the hands of the chemical industry, the source of an
unimaginable variety of valuable materials. The commonly accepted figure of speech which makes a gold
mine the symbol of the greatest potential value is en-

tirely inadequate to express the wealth of usefulness which the magic of chemists and the earnest labor of the chemical industry have created from this formerly wasted product of coal. The hues of the rainbow are as nothing compared with the range of colors and shades of our synthetic dyes; modern medicine could not cope with disease except through the beneficent help of the vast number of synthetic drugs owing their ultimate origin to coal-tar; and the perfumes of Nature's flowers are less varied than those produced in quantity from this evil smelling raw material. One could readily exhaust the whole gamut of superlatives in description of the accomplishments of organic chemists, made useful by the chemical industry, in creating beauty and value from common coal-tar.

Chemical elaboration of compounds found in petroleum and natural gas has yielded for the United States an industry unique in the world and new within two decades. Our lavish use of a bountiful supply of crude oil has familiarized every American with gasoline and lubricating and fuel oils directly made from petroleum. Other important materials now made by chemical industry from the same source are less familiar. Quite characteristically, none of them reveal the slightest trace of their origin in an oil well.

In dealing with these raw materials, a variety of technics has necessarily been developed. The methods of winning metals from their ores naturally differ in important particulars from those employed in converting coal-tar into its derivatives. The recovery of alkalies and bleaching agents from common salt involves a very different type of operation from that employed in making artificial stones of enormous hardness from coke and sand or boric acid. Thus, one finds great sections of the industry engaged in different kinds of operations, one imitating in its factories under careful control the processes occurring in the intense, wild heat of the volcano, another utilizing under similar precise control temperatures far colder than any to be found on the earth, even in the darkest Arctic night, and so on through a wide diversity of operations and conditions necessitated by them. It is improper to speak of these different parts of the chemical industry as *divisions,* for the solidarity of the whole does not permit splitting it into parts. Rather they may be considered to be branches which together constitute a single industry as the branches of a tree are integral parts of a single unit.

Two great branches are those dealing with organic or living things and with inorganic or lifeless matter. The distinction between the two dates back to the remote past when it was believed that vital force, the force of life, was essential to the wide variety of chemical changes occurring in the living matter of plants and animals and that this made it forever impossible for them to be duplicated in the laboratory. The distinction has largely vanished as science and industry have continued their explorations into the unknown and have demonstrated their ability to effect transformations even beyond those attempted by Nature. Today, the term organic chemistry is applied as a merely convenient designation to what we know of the compounds of carbon—which largely make up living things—and inorganic chemistry deals with everything else, principally those materials derived from the minerals of the earth.

To understand the chemical industry it is necessary to consider these important branches and the smaller ones which constitute them, as well as the basic conceptions of the science on which the whole is founded. We have already noted that the explorations of scientists into the unknown secrets of Nature nourish the tree of chemical industry. These explorations take two important forms; *analysis,* by which the constituents of Nature's, as well as man's, products are determined by the more or less obvious process of taking them apart, and *synthesis,* which is the putting together, the building up, of the constituent parts of materials into familiar or new forms. The period of analysis characterized science, particularly chemistry, during the nineteenth century. It is improper to imply that all things have been analyzed and their constituents learned, but it is important to realize that a long period of following this lead was an essential precursor of the present period of synthesis which has been so fruitful of good to mankind. While analysis confines itself to known materials, synthesis in an important way includes within its purview the building up not only of known materials, but, what is even more valuable, the preparation of utterly new kinds of matter without prototypes anywhere in nature. It is this exploring synthesis which has yielded vast numbers of the vitally important materials of modern medicine and of modern living which

25

so largely free us from the dread of disease and from the drudgery and drabness of the lives of our forebears.

So important has become the synthesis of organic compounds that the branch of the industry devoted to this manufacture, the synthetic organic chemical industry, has come to typify the whole chemical industry in the minds of many people. Its products cover the widest range of interest and utility: from the dyes whose variety shames Nature's meager offering, the perfumes and flavors which delight our noses and palates with new sensations, the chemical agents important in our national security, the synthetic resins, without which the innumerable articles so convenient in our daily lives would be impossible, and most vital of all— the modern medicines which alleviate our sufferings and prevent and cure disease. Such is the nature of this branch of chemical industry that practically any organization within it is able to convert its output almost in the twinkling of an eye from one group of these products to the other with little or no outwardly manifest change. While this convertibility of output is an outstanding characteristic of chemical manufacture generally, it is particularly true of this branch.

The fundamental branch of inorganic chemical industry is the extremely important manufacture of heavy chemicals, so-called on account of the huge quantities regularly consumed. Its output supplies the basis upon which all chemical industry rests. The acids and the alkalies constitute the most important products of this branch. In addition it is engaged in the elaboration of countless mineral ores into chemical compounds of value and importance to other industrial activities. Its field of activity approaches closely that of metallurgy, which is primarily occupied with winning metals in useful forms from their ores.

An interesting example of the prime importance and diversity of uses of a single group of chemicals, the very names of which are unknown to the average layman, is found in chromium products. Bichromate of soda, the most important of these, is a basic raw material in the tanning of leather and in the preparation of many pigments and paints. Its derivative, chromic acid, is used for all chromium plating, the applications of which have been so spectacularly widespread, and so durably handsome, whether used on automobile accessories, bathroom fixtures, panelled walls or modernistic furniture. Chromium compounds are also widely used as oxidizing agents in pickling and etching brass, copper and aluminum, fur tanning and dyeing, petroleum refining, gelatin hardening, bleach for paper making, photography, in the manufacture of green glass, ceramic glazes, blueprint paper, writing ink, insecticides, wood preservatives, matches, window shades, printers' rollers, khaki cloth, artificial roofing shingles, pyrotechnics, explosives, quinone, benzoates, artificial camphor, synthetic perfumes, and in inhibiting corrosion of all the common structural metals. It is interesting that so little known a group of chemicals should play so far-reaching a part in the development of durability, comfort, and beauty in modern life.

Other branches of chemical industry are characterized by the technic employed for their diverse operations. Thus, one finds an electrochemical branch whose operations are based upon the use of the electric current to effect chemical changes, and the relatively new industry of thermal chemistry which utilizes extraordinarily high temperatures, far greater than any otherwise used, to convert plentiful raw materials into useful forms. On the other extreme the unimaginable cold of liquid air is opening new fields.

Reference has already been made to the utilization of the products of agriculture through chemical transformation, but it remains to point out the significance of wider use of farm crops in the economics of the basic activity of agriculture. Primarily concerned with the production of food, our farms utilize the energy of sunlight through the green leaves of plants to synthesize cellulose, starches, sugars, fats, and proteins in enormous quantities. These constitute the basic foodstuffs and are to be synthesized industrially only with the greatest difficulty, if at all. In addition to their vital importance as foods, these agricultural products provide starting materials from which synthetic chemistry derives a vast number of industrially valuable products. The starches and sugars derived from them yield important solvents when fermented and a variety of other synthetic materials are produced from these by chemical industry. Ethyl alcohol, butyl alcohol, amyl alcohol, acetone, acetic acid, and other products of fermentation are made to undergo chemical changes which add new values to their inherent services to industry. Soy beans, tung nuts, maize, cottonseed, flax seed, and castor beans, among other farm crops, yield oils of significant industrial value in many fields. Milk produces casein of many diverse uses.

Recently emphasis has been placed on the industrial consumption of farm products and the growing of special crops for this use by the formation of a co-operative group of representatives of science, industry and agriculture. The growing of drug crops, long studied by the U. S. Department of Agriculture, of cellulose-producing plants, of plants rich in starches and sugars and of the various seeds which yield important paint oils has been particularly emphasized as a method of improving the economic status of our great agricultural industry. Enthusiastic proponents of this idea found upon investigation that chemical industry already is an important consumer of many crops and is in a very cordial sense promoting the idea on its part by encouraging agriculture in every way possible to meet its needs.

Through its intimate relation with and reliance upon the science of chemistry, chemical industry shares its knowledge of the fundamental nature of materials. Similarities between subtle perfumes and the most deadly poisons are obvious alike to the chemist in his laboratory and the manufacturer in his chemical plant. Like the laboratory of the chemist, its larger counterpart, the chemical manufactory, is adapted at the will of the operator to producing many various materials as they may be required by the demands of trade or the emergencies of war. Like his scientific confrère, the manufacturing chemist looks upon his task as the conversion of a raw material into a finished product of value rather than as simply the production of some specific commodity. The mobility which this imparts to the chemical industry is at once its greatest stabilizing force in a constantly changing world and its most important service to civilization in permitting it readily to keep abreast of the advances of science.

As a result of this innate mobility of action, the development of chemical enterprises has frequently brought together activities quite obviously unrelated from the layman's point of view. An explosive manufacturer finds himself led, by chemical similarities, to the simultaneous production of paints, fabrics, and colors. An operator of brine wells for the recovery of salt sees nothing incongruous in developing his manufacture to include the latest marvels of medicine, a new metal of striking value, and a fluid for use in power boilers, giving them an efficiency unattainable with steam alone. A manufacturer of medicines finds that his position is strengthened by producing at the same time a synthetic resin and a variety of chemicals used by the rubber manufacturer to improve the usefulness of his tires. These developments are characteristically American and fully illustrate the ramifications of chemical industry, both as showing the high type of Yankee ingenuity behind them and as typifying industrial chemical progress. Instances of this kind could be multiplied almost endlessly, but those mentioned will suffice to show that, within chemical industries, the hen mothers the duckling, and the cat the puppy, to such an extent that these exceptions become the rule.

In the fiscal structure of the industry, this tendency toward mobility of output has resulted in three logical directions of growth based upon (1) complete elaboration of a single raw material, (2) extension of a specialized technic of manufacture into many useful fields, and (3) development of a complete system of manufacture to supply all of the needs of a particular type of consumer industry. Into the first class fall the chemical manufacturing activities of the large petroleum companies, the development of broad manufacture on the basis of possession of brine, natural gas wells or ore deposits of an unusual character, and enterprises devoted to the manufacture of extensive lists of products made by the elaboration of coal-tar. The second type is illustrated by the activities of leading makers of dyes who have amplified their output by the inclusion of synthetic drugs and perfume raw materials. The third class is composed of organizations whose output has been diversified to include as many items as possible to be marketed by a single sales organization. For instance, a single firm might seek to supply all the wide variety of chemicals consumed by the textile industry, by rubber manufacturers, or by tanners of leather.

These three methods of development not infrequently progress simultaneously within the same organization and yield enterprises which have come to be known as "depression proof." It is, of course, untrue that the fluctuations of the economic cycle do not affect chemical companies, but even a cursory study of the record will show that they possess a stability unique in a wavering world. This stability has been built up through growth in somewhat the manner outlined, but an even more important factor has been and will continue to be the fundamentally important service rendered by this industry even in depressions to humanity's needs.

The idea of service, as embodied in the codes of ethics of the various professions has, as a rule, been paramount in the chemical industries. Outstanding examples of the rule, and some flagrant exceptions, could be cited. Nevertheless, the community of interest within chemical industry and its close contact with the professions of chemistry, medicine and engineering have been influential in creating an atmosphere unlike that to be found elsewhere in our industrial life.

These ideals are everywhere exemplified in the continuing contributions of this industry to the larger and fuller life of our people. The many ramifications of this service to humanity reach out in most amazing ways to affect all our activities. It is to the discussion of some of these that the following chapters will be devoted, rather than to a greater elaboration of the technicalities of the industry itself.

3.

Keeping Well

HUMANITY'S priceless possession is health. To its preservation chemical industry contributes enormously in
supplying materials for the prevention and cure of
disease. In reviewing this phase of chemical industry's
gifts to civilization, we must not lose sight of the fact
that it is only in the hands of the physician, qualified
by long and careful training, that any material can be
properly and intelligently used in treating the ailments
of the human body. Science long ago forsook its quest
for a universal remedy for all diseases. Only charlatans
still would have us believe, to their profit and not infrequently to our hurt, that they have found the long-
sought panacea. To discuss the whole broad subject of

health and disease is quite impossible here, but rather our attention will be directed toward the outstanding accomplishments in safeguarding health and curing disease to which chemical industry has signally contributed. The subject will be divided into three major phases: prevention of disease, alleviation of suffering, and specific cure of specific maladies.

Natural hazards from disease have been magnified to enormous proportions by the accumulation within small areas of vast populations drawing their supplies from common sources and disposing of their wastes in similarly large concentrations. Contacts from person to person are multiplied by community living. While this factor has had a beneficent influence in building up the immunity of whole populations to many diseases in a way impossible with savage peoples, it has greatly increased the danger of spread of communicable diseases. Plagues of the magnitude of those so prominent in the history of the Middle Ages are practically unknown today in populations several fold denser than the most concentrated of that time. That this is true is clearly traceable to our more intimate knowledge of the nature of diseases and the methods of their spread and to the application of that knowledge by the guardians of our health using the products supplied for their use by the chemical industry.

Primitive civilizations, in which may be included even the present state of living in some more sparsely populated sections, were practically free from many of the dangers to life and health which continually threaten urban populations. Not only are contacts between persons minimized among scattered peoples, but at no point in such communities is there an accumulation of wastes of either persons or manufacture of any dangerous proportions. Where the family is the unit of population supplying its own principal services in the form of food, drink and the other essentials of living, the problems of public health reduce themselves practically to those of individual personal hygiene. On the other hand, the increase in person-to-person contact inherent in city life not only multiplies the possibility of exposure to disease, but at the same time significantly increases the importance of other means for its dissemination. Instead of drawing its water supply from a source which can be carefully watched and guarded by the householder, the large community of families must depend upon a common supply whose volume makes the problem of safeguarding it an entirely different one. Similarly food and milk come from larger sources of supply less easily controlled by the individual and only to be safeguarded by concerted action of all the individuals of the group. The normal wastes of a community of persons are concentrated to a dangerous point, and their industrial activities produce a new set of objectionable wastes which must be dissipated.

Community watchfulness of supplies must be regarded as the most essential point in community health. The treatment of water supplies to make them safely potable usually requires filtration and sterilization; and for both of these operations, products of chemical industry are essential. The coagulation of water-borne impurities into aggregates which can be removed by filtration is usually accomplished by the addition of aluminum sulfate—related to the alums and produced from aluminum ores and sulfuric acid—and lime—made by burning limestone at a high temperature and slaking the product with water. This and similar treatments, generally applied to turbid water and frequently to clear water suspected of pollution, form in the water a coagulated jelly-like mass which enmeshes not only suspended particles of mud and silt but also many of the bacteria which, if not removed, are far more dangerous to health. There are in the United States 1545 such filter plants clarifying public supplies of drinking water and having a combined capacity of about 3.5 billions of gallons daily. The quantities of coagulants thus used are small in relation to the volume of water they purify and are removed by the filters so that none of either is detectable in the filtered water except by the most refined methods of analysis.

The introduction of filtration of public water supplies in the United States occurred many decades ago, but the first modern efficient filtration plants were built shortly after 1910, when chlorination was first used as a method of sterilizing drinking water. Chlorination consists in the introduction continuously into the water supply of a very small amount of chlorine, either the gas itself or bleaching powder made by combining the gas with lime. The amount of chlorine thus introduced is adjusted to the characteristics of the raw water in such a way as to secure practically complete sterilization and combination of the chlorine between the time of its introduction and the use of the water. The result of the combined filtration and chlorination is drinking water free from dirt and disease-causing bacteria. For sterilizing water some 35,000 tons of chlorine are used annually.

During the past six years the scope of usefulness of activated carbon has been much enlarged by its introduction into the field of water purification. At the present time between 800 and 1000 water purification plants depend upon activated carbon as the best means of insuring to the public palatable water at all times of the year. It is true that chlorine has for many years provided a germ-free water, but until the advent of activated carbon, many waters—although quite safe for drinking purposes—were at times unpalatable as compared with clear, spring water. The function of powdered, activated carbon is to absorb and remove from the water, impurities contained in the water or resulting from prior chemical treatment of water.

Certain disagreeable inhabitants of open impounded water supplies, known as algæ, impart an objectionable taste to the water containing them and cause undue alarm. To cure this condition other cleansing agents, among which is copper sulfate, are introduced in tiny proportions into reservoirs to prevent their growth. The quantities of copper sulfate used for this purpose are too small to evaluate as compared with the immense quantities utilized otherwise, but its importance when needed to clear up such an infestation is tremendous.

The same types of treatment used to purify potable water are applied to water used industrially for washing and to that used in swimming pools, otherwise active spreaders of a variety of diseases. A by-product obtained from oat hulls (furfural) is used to treat the bathing beaches of a well-known midwestern city (Madison, Wisconsin) to prevent the annoying infection known as swimmer's itch. The same chemical is used to treat swimming pools, locker rooms, and other possible sites of infection to prevent the spread of athlete's foot. Numerous other treatments are also important in fitting natural waters for special uses.

In the treatment of public water supplies, it is impossible to estimate accurately the individual effects of filtration or of subsequent sterilization on the actual number of human lives saved by them, so closely are they bound together. It is even impossible to secure an accurate estimate of their combined effect because so many causes are operating simultaneously to suppress the diseases normally attributable to water supply.

In attempting to evaluate the importance of treatment of water supplies, conclusions can only be based on very accurate, carefully gathered statistics of the occurrence of certain diseases before and after the general introduction of the methods of purification. The most important disease for this purpose is typhoid fever. However, during the period covered by statistics, many forces have been at work to reduce the incidence of this disease and consequently it is quite impossible to draw exact conclusions from these figures. If, with these qualifications, we assume that the typhoid-fever rate will give us some suggestion of the effectiveness of water treatment, the attached graphic representation of the conquest of this disease indicates the tremendous value

of the activities of the chemical industry in this field.
The graph of typhoid death rate in selected groups
of cities shows the pronounced effect of water purifica-

CHLORINATED WATER AND TYPHOID DEATH RATE
(CITIES OF 100,000-250,000 POPULATION)

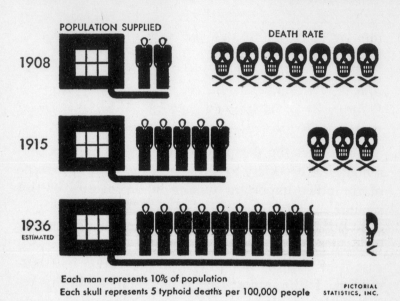

Each man represents 10% of population
Each skull represents 5 typhoid deaths per 100,000 people

PICTORIAL
STATISTICS, INC.

tion on this disease. Statistics for the whole United
States are impossible to obtain. However, the following tabulation is the closest approximation to nation-
wide figures. It will be noted that these figures are
given for registered areas and for registered states. The
use of the term "registered" in this connection is to
designate those areas and those states in which the law
requires the gathering of complete statistics.

KEEPING WELL

DEATH RATE FROM TYPHOID FEVER IN THE UNITED STATES

(Deaths per 100,000 population)

YEAR	REGISTERED AREAS	REGISTERED STATES
1910	23.4	22.5
1915	12.4	10.4
1920	7.8	5.3
1925	8.0	4.0
1930	4.8	2.1
1934	3.3	(1933) 1.3

To correct the perspective of the picture thus presented, it is necessary to consider at the same time some of the other important factors in the control of this scourge.

It is a fact well known to medicine that the proper disposal of body wastes carrying the germs of the disease is of essential importance in preventing its transmission. If the utmost care is not exercised in this respect, the spread of typhoid in areas of relatively dense population is inescapable. Not only is it probable that water supplies, used subsequent to the introduction of sewage before the natural processes of self-purification have had an opportunity to operate, will carry the germs to new victims, but also dangerous accumulation of them in streams disperses fish and makes shellfish carriers of disease with no outward signals that they are unfit for food.

This consideration applies particularly to those things

41

directly taken into the system as food and drink, but a similar danger lurks in the use for washing purposes of contaminated water which, while presuming to clean, actually deposits germs in places where they are sure to reach human victims. The dairy industry, because it deals in milk, a material especially adapted for the growth of micro-organisms of all kinds, must exercise particular care to prevent the contamination of its output in this way. Bleaching powder, chlorine, numerous alkaline salts and soaps, all products of chemical industry, are used in large quantities by this industry to cleanse its equipment and utensils and thus to keep our milk and cream supplies free from bacterial impurities.

These methods of preserving the public health are directed at the harm after it has been turned loose. Even more important are the measures taken by municipalities to prevent their wastes from being turned loose in dangerously toxic form. The chain of communication between the source of germs and their possible victim is most effectively broken by preventing the escape and dissemination of the germs as near their point of origin as possible. This consideration has led to the recent rapid growth of the art of treatment and scientific disposal of sewage.

Sewage treatment takes several distinct forms. Earliest efforts were directed to the disinfection by lime or otherwise of the body wastes of persons as soon as produced—measures which could be easily and properly applied in the individual household. The spread of modern sanitary plumbing accumulated the wastes of whole populations and, while removing the source of contamination from the household, produced a much more serious problem at some other point. The application of the method used by the individual householder was too expensive and too inefficient to be used on a large scale. The process by which nature purifies streams consists primarily in causing intimate contact between the waste material and immense volumes of air. By intensifying and controlling this process, the so-called activated sludge process was developed to remove contamination from even so concentrated a source as city sewage.

Other methods depend on the chemical precipitation of solid matter from sewage. In addition to the activated sludge process and chemical precipitation, the destruction of solid matter contained in the sewage is accomplished by the action of bacteria in decomposing the organic products contained and forming gases useful for power and heat, after which the remaining solids are separated. The ultimate result of such methods now used by the principal cities of the world is to remove from sewage before it is allowed to escape all possible danger of its carrying disease. At the same time, chemical treatment and refinement are applied to separate from the resulting sterile effluent certain valuable elements that can be returned safely to the soil as fertilizing materials.

Wastes of industry frequently contain potential danger to water supply. This may take several forms: noxious substances which are disagreeable if not actually dangerous in themselves; nutrient materials which promote the increase of contamination in streams by

43

serving as food for micro-organisms; and actual bacteria which may be dangerous. The first class of wastes are those vented by dyehouses and certain chemical manufacturing plants containing residual amounts of material in too low concentrations to pay for their recovery. Starch factories, breweries and most of the food-handling industries discharge wastes as sewage containing nutrient materials on which micro-organisms thrive. Tannery wastes contain large numbers of bacteria whose growth has been necessary to the performance of certain operations in the making of leather.

For the preservation of the health of the community, these trade wastes must be prevented from reaching streams which ultimately serve as sources of potable water. Often, under the necessity of preventing the escape of such wastes, plant executives have found ways of modifying their operations or of recovering values that make this process of preserving public health an asset on the company's books instead of an expense. The case of a large starch manufacturing plant is a case in point, for it was found that values could be recovered by modifying the process and other values secured by relatively simple chemical treatment which more than paid the cost of processing. Instances of this kind could be multiplied to demonstrate the profit to be derived from preventing such noxious wastes, but suffice it to say here that danger to public health from this cause is vanishingly small today.

For the purposes of sewage treatment and the recovery of values from it, chemical industry supplies a wide variety of useful materials: precipitating agents to

44

coagulate suspended matter and allow it to be separated, treating agents to make otherwise disagreeable substances harmless, absorbents, special charcoals and the like, to remove disagreeable materials from even dilute solutions, and many other beneficent agents to minimize or prevent contamination.

The absorbent charcoals have come to occupy so important a place in the purification of a wide variety of materials that some further word about them will not be amiss. During the World War, when chemical weapons were first used on a large scale, the property of charcoal to absorb minute amounts of impurities from gases was considered the simplest and most effective protective measure against "poison gas." The most effective charcoal was to be had from the pits of peaches and plums and from cocoanut shells. To gather these raw materials in quantities great enough to meet the need, barrels for their collection were placed at almost every street crossing in our larger cities and the chemical industry undertook to convert these pits into acceptable charcoal for gas protection. In the course of the investigation of methods of doing this, ways were found to increase many fold the effectiveness of ordinary carbon and today these "activated carbons," as they are called, are supplied in huge tonnages to many industries to remove odors and impurities from their products.

Chemical industry has obviously done much to prevent disease from being carried from one person to another by ordinary supplies of food and water. It has further aided in the same prevention of contagion by

45

developing the large class of germ-killing materials known as disinfectants.

Lister, building upon the pioneer conceptions of Pasteur, was the first to apply disinfectants successfully in our fight against disease. Pasteur originated the important concept that many diseases are caused by micro-organisms and that these can be killed by heat and by certain chemical materials poisonous to them. Lister developed the latter phase of the idea and applied it to surgical technic and to the prevention of the spread of disease from patient to patient in hospitals. Since that time, an unceasing search has been carried on to devise and create germicides of such a character that they will exterminate microbial life without otherwise causing injury or damage.

As a result of this constant searching, thousands of substances have been found which kill germ life under the widest variety of conditions. Some of these occur naturally (salt, fresh air and sunlight), but most of them are created or purified in the works of the chemical industry. Phenol (carbolic acid) refined from coaltar, alcohol, chlorine, iodine, compounds of mercury, silver, copper, arsenic, and other metals, formaldehyde and sulfur dioxide, produced by the burning of sulfur in the air, are among the most vigorous and potent enemies of germ life. From these through a wide range of modifications and combinations of them conceived by organic chemists and produced by the chemical industry, to such mild disinfectants as boric acid and hydrogen peroxide, the range of germ killers would seem to be complete.

46

Nevertheless, the search continues for killers whose selective action is so precise that they will destroy only certain germ cells without injuring the cells of the living person within whose body they cause disease. The technic of selective destruction of the germs of disease was first developed through the use of quinine to cure malarial fevers. Later, this same idea was given vigorous life by Ehrlich, who succeeded in preparing synthetically a chemical compound which would destroy the germs of syphilis without injuring the patient. One thus recognizes among the many disinfectants available through the operations of the chemical industry some having the character of the most destructive high explosive shells which lay waste all the territory in their path; and from these wholesale destroyers their range extends to an accuracy comparable to the trained technic of an expert rifleman whose aim is unerring. The great scourges, spread through accumulated infectious matter, as is typhoid fever; the intermittent fever of malaria; and specific infectious diseases like syphilis; each of these is amenable to preventive or curative treatment with materials devised by research chemists, manufactured by the chemical industry, and applied by physicians.

In addition to man's continuous war on the germs of disease, he must also be constantly awake to the dangers from hordes of insects which not only compete with the human race for foods, but which act as carriers for the germs of many diseases. In the latter role, insects seem to have been allied by Nature with these invisible enemies of men and by this alliance have multiplied the germs' area of attack and magnified their maliciousness.

One has but to mention the plague of yellow fever (now happily almost exterminated) and of malaria carried by particular varieties of mosquitoes, the disease-carrying proclivities of sewage-loving house flies, and countless other insect pests to realize their extreme seriousness to us. Thanks to the ceaseless warfare waged upon them in every quarter, using the weapons supplied by chemical industry, many of the most dangerous insects have been so decimated as to be comparatively harmless; and the increasing vigor of the attack on them, as new strategies are developed by entomologists and new weapons are supplied by a chemical industry ever alert to utilize the latest findings of scientists, promises an end of fear from this source. One has but to recall the extraordinary rapidity of reproduction of insects to realize the necessity for protection.

The spread of disease by rats and by the common house fly has been the cause of innumerable epidemics. The fight against them is too recent for its watchwords to have died out of present memory. "Swat the fly" is no longer an essential on every billboard, as it was a very few years ago. In the campaigns which conquered these enemies of man, chemical industry supplied many of the most important and effective weapons.

Among the specific preventives of certain diseases, none are more important than the vaccines and sera which have been developed to confer immunity upon persons to whom they are administered. Nearly two centuries ago, Jenner discovered that matter from sores on a cow which had a disease known as cow-pox could

48

produce this disease in human beings in a form so mild as to be perfectly safe and that, thereafter, that individual could not contract the dread plague of smallpox. This important discovery formed the basis of long and careful scientific investigations in the intervening years and finally was amplified by other workers to the point where the manufacture of vaccines from the blood of various livestock has become an essential part of the chemical industry. Although the processes involved are strictly biological, the technic of handling them has been developed by the chemical industry to supplement its production of other medicinal essentials and to insure that the same careful manipulation required in other lines is applied to this one.

In addition to the preventive vaccine which has practically wiped out smallpox among the plagues of mankind, similar treatments have been developed, and are produced in quantity, which act with the utmost certainty in preventing tetanus, hydrophobia, diphtheria, and in livestock canine distemper, rabies, and hog cholera. In addition, there are numerous other diseases—scarlet fever, the common cold, and spinal meningitis—for which similar treatments are partially successful.

The value of the application of serums and vaccines in the prevention and alleviation of these dread diseases is principally evident in the fact that none of them is now a universal plague, as each was within relatively few decades. To accomplish this desirable result, it has been necessary to perfect methods of manufacture of these specific remedial agents on such a scale and at such economy of labor and materials that the whole population could be inoculated against these diseases. This has been a development of chemical industry, applying the discoveries of biologists and medical investigators. So successful has it been that the whole cost to the people of the United States of these necessary preventive agents has been of the order of five million dollars annually. The economic value of these expenditures to the country is positively immeasurable since there is no possible standard of comparison available of a similar populace in which these prophylactic steps have been omitted. Obviously, however, if one assigns an arbitrary economic value of $5000 to a human life, the whole bill for these preventives of disease will have been met if 1000 people are saved annually through their use. It is quite apparent that the over-all economic profit to the whole population reaches enormous totals quite regardless of humanitarian considerations impossible to evaluate in economic terms.

While properly a subject to be discussed in connection with the food supply and the selection of the most efficient dietary, the vitamins are equally related to preventive medicine. Early in the twentieth century, careful research revealed that in addition to the fundamental foodstuffs from which we derive the energy and materials for our bodies, there must be present in our daily dietary certain other substances whose nature is even yet not fully understood but which, in some extraordinary way, enable our digestive systems to function properly and our bodies to assimilate and utilize foods. Their existence was first discovered by the fact that lack of them caused certain diseases and the word "vita-

mins" was coined to designate these essential food factors. Several types of vitamins were differentiated whose
absence from the diet produced specific symptoms and
pathological changes in the individual. Because the
various vitamins were known only by their effects, they
were designated alphabetically as vitamins A, B, C, and
so on. The following tabulation shows the accepted
vitamins and the principal facts now known about
them.

VITAMINS

	FUNCTIONS	IMPORTANT SOURCES
VITAMIN A	1. Growth 2. Prevention of "dry eye infection" 3. Better resistance to infection in many parts of the body 4. Long life 5. Essential for mothers to bear and nurse strong babies	1. Cod-liver oil 2. Halibut-liver oil 3. Carrots 4. Spinach 5. Tomatoes 6. Butter 7. Egg yolk 8. Whole milk 9. Cream 10. Beef liver 11. Turnip tops 12. Mustard greens
VITAMIN B	1. Growth 2. Appetite 3. Good digestion 4. Greater nervous sta-bility 5. Essential for mothers to bear and nurse strong babies 6. Prevention of beri-beri	1. Yeast 2. Wheat germ 3. Whole grain cereals 4. Egg yolk 5. Whole milk 6. Peas 7. Tomatoes 8. Spinach 9. Beans 10. Asparagus 11. Carrots 12. Liver

VITAMINS—*Continued*

	FUNCTIONS	IMPORTANT SOURCES
VITAMIN C	1. Well-nourished gums and teeth 2. Better blood vessels 3. Growth 4. Prevention of scurvy 5. Protects against deterioration of bone	1. Oranges 2. Lemons 3. Tomatoes 4. Pineapples 5. Grapefruit 6. Strawberries 7. Peas 8. Cabbage (raw) 9. Greens 10. Peppers
VITAMIN D	1. Sound teeth 2. Strong bones 3. Prevention of rickets	1. Halibut-liver oil 2. Cod-liver oil 3. Egg yolk 4. Milk or cream reinforced with vitamin D
VITAMIN G	1. Growth 2. Better chance of long life 3. Better appetite 4. Factor in prevention of pellagra	1. Yeast 2. Liver 3. Kidney 4. Beef 5. Wheat germ 6. Spinach 7. Egg 8. Milk 9. Prunes 10. Turnip tops 11. Carrots 12. Asparagus

OTHER VITAMINS

Recent research investigations are confirming the existence of other vitamins besides those listed and described above. At present the facts regarding the functions and distribution of these new vitamins are not firmly enough established to justify their being listed in this chart. *(Courtesy H. J. Heinz Co.)*

Although strenuous efforts have been made to synthesize these essential materials, and some of them have reached that goal, it is still necessary to depend upon natural sources for supplies needed to prevent and cure the diseases vitamin deficiency is known to cause. Chemical industry, particularly that part of it devoted to the supplying of the needs of the medical profession, has served by concentrating from huge masses of natural materials these essential parts. Such concentrates possess the special advantage that they can be administered in exact doses without large amounts of diluting substances whose presence might be disagreeable or even harmful to the patient. For example, vitamin A is known to exist in fish-liver oils, notably those of cod and halibut. The dosages of cod-liver oil sometimes required would be so great that the quantity of oil that must be consumed to insure a proper amount of vitamin might cause serious disturbances of the digestive system. In addition, the vitamin is in no respect essential to the other uses of the same oil, for example by the tanning industry in the finishing of leather. Methods have been devised and are now industrially applied to huge quantities of this oil which concentrate the vitamin content of a ton of oil in a few ounces of potent extract. The concentrate is effective in much diminished doses where the use of the untreated oil would require that the patient take actual quarts to obtain even less curative effect. Halibut-liver oil contains some hundred times as great a proportion of vitamin A as cod-liver oil and hence needs no special concentrating for use. Vitamin B is so disperse in rice polishings that ten tons of raw

53

material yield only an ounce of vitamin. In a similar way, concentrates of the other vitamins from natural sources have placed at the disposal of physicians potent weapons against many diseases resulting from our increasing tendency to confine our choice of foods to highly refined modern products.

The industrial production of vitamin concentrates, which yield in small compass the effective parts of large masses of materials, has already reached substantial proportions. The value produced in better health by the proper application of these products and their increasing use is beyond present ability to estimate. As research reveals the actual composition of the various vitamins, we may anticipate that the pure substances will be made generally available through synthetic processes similar to those which have given us the colors which so brighten our lives and the remedial agents of modern medicine. One of them, vitamin C, is already being commercially synthesized and the production of vitamin D by irradiation is the virtual equivalent of synthesis. Others will undoubtedly follow.

One of the vitamins, vitamin D, requires special discussion, for the lack of it caused by modern methods of living has been universally evident and serious in its effects on the whole population of our large cities. This vitamin is responsible for the proper assimilation within our bodies of the element calcium which forms an essential part of bones and teeth. The lack of it has been definitely convicted of responsibility for rickets and for what are commonly known as soft teeth. The most remarkable thing about this vitamin is that it can be produced in many different materials, particularly those containing various oils, and even within our bodies themselves by exposure to the sun's rays. Further investigation revealed that not all of sunlight is equally effective in producing the vitamin but only what are known as ultra-violet rays, light of a wave length too short to be visible. It is possible to introduce this food essential into many foodstuffs by exposing them to the right kind of light. Special lamps of various kinds, mercury vapor lamps and carbon arc lights particularly, have been devised of materials supplied by chemical industry to furnish these bone-improving rays. For this purpose, mercury vapor excited by an electric current is confined within a bulb or tube of pure fused quartz, since ordinary glass will not easily permit the passage of the healing rays. Although the carbons ordinarily used in arc lights produce ultra-violet light, specially treated carbons, containing other elements found by extensive research to be effective, yield a light richer in vitamin-producing radiation.

Quite as important in our dietary requirements as the vitamins are many chemical elements. Many of these—iron, calcium, phosphorus—are required in substantial quantities since they enter into the general tissues of the body in considerable proportions. Others —iodine, copper—are required in relatively small amounts for special effects on body functions. These five elements are so vital, particularly to the growing infant, that foods must be selected to supply them in satisfactory abundance. Still other mineral elements—magnesium, sodium, potassium, manganese, chlorine and sulfur—are supplied by ordinary diet in sufficient quantities to meet the body's needs.

MINERALS IN FOODS

	FUNCTIONS	IMPORTANT SOURCES
CALCIUM	1. Strong bones 2. Sound teeth 3. Steady nerves 4. Clotting of blood 5. Balance among mineral elements 6. Prevention of rickets	1. Milk 2. Cheese 3. Egg yolk 4. Turnip tops 5. Spinach 6. Cauliflower 7. Beans 8. Kale 9. Celery 10. Turnips 11. Nuts
PHOS-PHORUS	1. Strong bones 2. Sound teeth 3. Building of body tissues 4. Prevention of rickets	1. Egg yolk 2. Cheese 3. Whole grain cereals 4. Peas 5. Beans 6. Carrots 7. Spinach 8. Peanuts 9. Milk 10. Chocolate 11. Liver
IRON	1. Essential element in all cells of the body 2. Enables red blood cells to carry oxygen to body tissues	1. Liver 2. Molasses 3. Whole grain cereals 4. Prunes 5. Apricots 6. Spinach 7. Oysters 8. Lean meat 9. Potatoes 10. Lettuce 11. Egg yolk 12. Asparagus

MINERALS IN FOODS—*Continued*

	FUNCTIONS	IMPORTANT SOURCE
COPPER	1. Necessary in minute amounts for utilization of iron by red blood cells 2. Poisonous in larger quantities	1. Liver 2. Shrimp 3. Oysters 4. Nuts 5. Leafy vegetables 6. Poultry 7. Peas 8. Whole grains
IODINE	1. Thyroid functioning 2. Prevention of simple goiter	1. Oysters 2. Shrimp 3. Clams 4. Salmon 5. Halibut 6. "Iodized" salt 7. Vegetables grown on soils of good iodine content

(Courtesy H. J. Heinz Co.)

So far, this discussion has dealt with potent factors in the prevention of disease. Chemical industry has functioned even more importantly in supplying the materials to alleviate suffering and to insure renewed health to those already suffering from the inroads of disease or the bodily discomfort of accident. One has but to compare yesterday with today; the confidence with which one today faces the surgeon's knife with the vividly contrasting picture of the crude surgery of a century ago; the skill displayed by modern surgeons in repairing or removing deep-seated organs of the body with the anxious activities of their forebears only a few decades ago when the opening of the abdominal cavity was a desperate measure which few patients survived; the cleanliness of the modern aseptic hospital with the pesthouses of the period of our Civil War, in which patients suffering from minor ailments were infected with all manner of diseases; to realize that the march of science has vastly improved our chances of survival from the most serious ailments.

To this great advance of medicine and surgery, two factors have been vitally and fundamentally important: the discovery of antiseptics and the application of anesthesia. Modern use of antiseptics prevents the infection of a patient suffering from one disorder with the germs of another and, as has already been pointed out in the discussion of the grosser agents for this purpose, has made absolute cleanliness possible. Without these potent materials for the destruction of contagion, surgery of the intricacy now practiced would merely result in the easier transmission of disease from one patient to another. Anesthesia's relaxing sleep, which renders the body amenable to the surgeon's treatment without pain and without interference through muscular contraction with the most delicate operation, and the many valuable local anesthetics, which confer insensibility to pain, have alone made it possible to mend our bodies in the marvellous ways that we have come to take as matters of course.

Without in any way detracting from the deep debt of gratitude the world owes to its patient students and expert practitioners of medical science, the chemical industry can justly claim with pride an important, even an essential, part in the performance of these daily miracles. It is, of course, impossible that these things could be done without the use of certain special materials to kill bacteria and to induce anesthetic sleep. These materials are produced by the chemical industry in quantities and at prices which make it needless for any human being to suffer for lack of them.

The potency of chlorine as an antiseptic in treating water supplies has been mentioned. Combined to form sodium hypochlorite, it is the active ingredient of Carrel-Dakin solutions so beneficently valuable in removing deep-seated infections in wounds in the body. General gangrenous poisoning produced when the tissue of the body is so seriously bruised as to prevent the proper flow of blood to the injured part yields easily to this powerful germicide and through its use countless lives have been saved. Many different forms of the familiar phenols, a term applied to a whole class of substances related to carbolic acid, formaldehyde produced from wood alchohol, and bichloride of mercury (corrosive sublimate), are of valuable assistance to medical cleanliness. Germicides having high effectiveness without causing injury to the human tissues may be recounted in numbers running into the hundreds, and each of these contributes its special value to assist in the alleviation and cure of disease.

Anesthesia induced deliberately for medical purposes is distinctly an American development dating from the period before our Civil War, when laughing gas (nitrous oxide) was a curiosity demonstrated as a sort of sideshow entertainment. This gas has the peculiar ability to render the person breathing it quite unconscious of his actions and surroundings and, in addition, enough of it produces entire insensibility to pain. At about the same time, sulfuric ether, so called because it was derived from ethyl alcohol by the action of sulfuric acid, was found to have a similar ability to induce sleep and insensibility to pain and was first used in anesthesia in 1842. After a sufficiently large number of trials to develop the method of use of these two substances, the modern era of surgery may be considered properly to have begun because it was now possible to cut, patch and mend the body of a living person with practically the ease and certainty that a skillful operator could dissect a cadaver. Lately, a mixture of ether, alcohol and thymol has been used in desensitizing teeth during drilling, as ether alone does the whole body, thus removing the fear of dental operations.

With the introduction of anesthesia, a new call was made upon chemical manufacturers to produce the essential materials and in co-operation with both medical and chemical research workers, studies were initiated to improve both the technic of anesthesia and the materials available for inducing it. Chloroform and its derivative, chloral hydrate, were similarly used but possessed drawbacks which prevented their universal acceptance. Later, other ethers chemically similar to sulfuric or ethyl ether were used—some of them with success. Most recent of the developments in this field, valuable because it avoids the retching and vomiting which usually follow prolonged anesthesia by ether, as well as because it somewhat reduces the liability of the patient to contract pneumonia after a serious operation,

ethylene has come into general but not yet universal favor with surgeons. It, too, is chemically related to ether and to ethyl or grain alcohol. Ethylene is prepared by passing alcohol vapors over heated purified clay and on an even larger scale by thermal decomposition of ethane of natural gas. It is a constituent of coal gas and of the waste gas from the manufacture of gasoline from petroleum by the cracking process. Like most chemical products, it finds many uses besides that of anesthesia. More important than this use is its easy conversion into a long list of valuable materials through chemical synthesis, a subject which will be considered in a later chapter.

Many minor operations of the surgeon can be conducted without requiring the complete unconsciousness of the patient if the pain attending upon his work can be alleviated. The first analgesic, as such pain deadeners are known, was cocaine derived from the leaves of a South American tree. Its first use was by the natives who were found by the earliest Spanish explorers to be accustomed to chew these leaves to relieve fatigue on long marches. Like many other products of Nature, coca leaves contain many other substances of no service in producing insensibility to pain and hence the early use of the leaves and of extracts derived directly from them were less successful than our present use of cocaine. Later, it was found possible to separate the cocaine from unwanted substances which it contained and thus its good effect was much enhanced. However, cocaine has bad qualities as well as good, among which is the property of making addicts of those who use it, causing an inordinate craving on the part of the user which, when continuously satisfied, leads to his complete undoing by destroying his mental equipment. One of the most important contributions of scientific chemical research to medicine resulted from the efforts of chemists to synthesize cocaine and from the study of the effects of various parts of its complex molecule. It was learned from these studies that one part of the molecule of cocaine induced insensibility to pain and quite another created the craving for the drug, while still another was the destructive agency in the degeneration of the addict. With this information as to the precise effect of each part of the cocaine molecule, the next step was that of creating a material having only the desired characteristics of cocaine without its undesirable ones. The result of this combined research of chemistry and medicine was finally materialized by the chemical industry into a substance known as procaine or novocaine, whose sole characteristic is the deadening of certain sensory nerves to pain. It is most largely used in dentistry in the extraction of teeth and in performing other operations in the mouth. This triumph of synthetic chemistry has been followed by the discovery and creation of many other beneficent drugs without counterparts anywhere in Nature. By pursuing the same line of investigation, it has been possible to create substances which induce sleep, as morphine does, without causing the other disturbances of the body that accompany its use. A whole family of extremely valuable drugs, derived from barbituric acid and entirely synthetic, gives the physician a control over the nervous

63

reaction of a patient quite impossible without them and thus enables him the better to effect the results required by the special circumstances of the case.

Medicines and pharmaceuticals generally are made by the chemical industry. Some of them are as simple as oxygen, itself an element, whose preparation for use consists essentially in separating from it the nitrogen which accompanies it in the air. When so separated it is the most effective means known for alleviating the suffering of pneumonia. Latterly, oxygen has been shown to be beneficial in angina pectoris (where it relieves the patient's shortness of breath) and in certain forms of insanity. Other medicines reach great complexity through the building up of numerous atoms into large molecules of special desired properties, such as modern hypnotics for inducing sleep and analgesics for deadening pain.

In addition to the numerous medicinal compounds which are synthesized by chemical industry, a vast number of potent materials are extracted and purified from leaves, barks, berries and roots of plants. This separating and purifying operation yields drugs which have been reduced to pure principles. The extraction of morphine, codeine, and other narcotics from the sap of the Oriental poppy, the separation of the alkaloids, quinine, cinchonidine, and others from Peruvian bark and the purification of atropine from belladonna leaves are typical of this service of the chemical industry to the healing art. Botanists have shown the way to grow the plants yielding important drugs within the continental United States and chemical industry has utilized these natural products to prepare pure and effective medicines.

Most medicines are alleviative in their action and not definitely curative. Rather, they overcome the symptoms of disease and give the patient a chance to recover. A very few actual curatives are known and these are generally classified as specifics, denoting thereby that they will definitely cure one disease and presumably no other.

Despite the centuries of experience of the race in the treatment of human diseases, there are now known but a mere handful of specific curative medicines. The first of these (and the one on which our whole theory of specific curatives is based) was the cure of malarial fever by the administration of quinine, derived from the bark of a South American tree. Quinine as Nature provides it is mixed with many other materials. Some of these are as harmful to the patient as quinine may be beneficial. When purified, it can be taken into the human system in such quantities as to destroy the parasite of malaria without in any way injuring the person in whose blood stream malaria is rampant. No other parasites are known for which quinine has the same toxicity and no other drug is known which similarly destroys this parasite.

The dread scourge of syphilis was attacked from this point of view and Ehrlich found that a certain type of organic compound of arsenic was effective in destroying the parasite of syphilis when administered in doses within the tolerance of the individual. Numerous other investigators have similarly studied other diseases and other synthetic drugs in the hope of finding others similarly sure in their action.

For quite a different group of diseases having very different characteristics, a whole set of specific remedies has been found. These diseases are caused by abnormal functioning of certain glands of the body whose products are turned into our blood streams and thus control in a most magical way the growth and functioning of our bodies. These substances, called hormones, are produced by the thyroid, pancreas, pineal, suprarenal, sex and other glands and any failure or overabundance of the required supply seriously upsets the normal metabolism of the body. In diseases known to be caused by malfunctioning of these glands, it is possible to introduce into the body corrective doses of the purified extracts of similar glands from animals and thus to effect a cure. Insulin, adrenalin, pituitrin and thyroxin are typical of the glandular principles extensively used in modern therapy for the cure of diseases caused by their deficiency. In a very similar way, it has lately been shown that pernicious anemia may be cured by introducing into the system the extract of fresh calves' livers which in some remarkable way stimulates the functioning of the blood-creating mechanism of the body.

These advances in medical science have, like the manufacture of the materials by which they are accomplished, resulted from long and painstaking researches. In the medical world, this type of research has been conducted on animals as well as men. In the chemical industry, research—sometimes of a similar character but more often very different—has preceded the manufac-

66

ture of the armamenta of the physician and often has even preceded the studies of medical research workers. In addition to conducting its own investigations of manufacturing problems, chemical industry has happily been able to lend its support, both morally and financially, to medical research workers in their constant battle to make life more secure from disease. The value of the solutions to some of the major problems of the cure of disease is quite incalculable. As but one example of what may be gained, it has been said that the discovery of a specific cure of African sleeping sickness (trypanosomiasis) would be equivalent to the discovery of a new continent, so large would be the territory this would open to human habitation.

The whole value of the basic materials of medicines produced by the chemical industry reaches an annual total of about 272 million dollars, a triflingly small amount to pay for this insurance of the health of the nation's people. At retail the people of the United States pay some 715 million dollars annually for medicines to treat some 100 million illnesses of all kinds (serious and slight) per annum.

4.

Feeding Millions

MORE than a century and a half ago, the eminent economist, Malthus, prophesied that in less than a hundred years the human race would cease to multiply on the earth because, according to his calculations, it would, by that time, be impossible to grow enough foodstuffs to feed them. Among the numerous important factors which have prevented the realization of this dire expectation, none has been more important than the contribution of chemical manufacture to the growth of foodstuffs by materializing the discovery of fertilizers by the chemist, Liebig. Populations greater in density than any anticipated by Malthus are comfortably supported now in a world to which exploration has added no important new territory in the intervening years and yet the areas available for agricultural purposes are far from completely occupied.

The development of the art of making many bushels of foodstuffs grow where one grew before connects, through the industry of fertilizer manufacture, numerous superficially unrelated things. Mines of chemical salts in Germany and the arid wastes of the American desert; rainless plains on the west coast of South America and the world's greatest war; prehistoric monsters that roamed the antediluvian continent of America and the coral polyps which still industriously build up its fringes; the harnessing of flood waters in some of our great rivers and the ice that preserves our foods from the farm to the table; all of these are parts of the story of fertilizer development from a series of experiments made by a German chemist nearly a century ago.

The original discovery was that the growth of plants ordinarily consumes several elements from the soil to the point of serious depletion and that, unless these are replaced from time to time, the yield from the land would ultimately diminish to the vanishing point as successive crops were harvested. Potassium, nitrogen, and phosphorus form such large and important parts of the structures of plants that the removal of each crop takes away a substantial part of the total supply available in any one place. By adding these elements to the soil in a form available for feeding the plants grown on it, the effect of these successive depletions can be avoided. That was one of the most important discoveries of a century of revolutionary advances, for not only did it provide a means of insuring the yield of existing agricultural lands, but at the same time it opened the way to the utilization of areas otherwise unprofitable to cultivate. This was the important step forward from the American Indian tradition of burying a dead fish in each hill of maize, for it revealed the reason for the fish's effectiveness and showed the way to improvement.

The story of commercial development of fertilizers emphasizes again what must be repeated often in the course of this discussion: the manifold utility, the multidexterity, if you will, of fundamental materials after they have passed through the refining and remaking processes of chemical manufacture. The multifarious applications of these elements of fertility will be evident in the following discussion of each of them individually, for it is difficult to be clear on the subject without separating them.

NITROGEN

Although nearly 80 per cent of the air we breathe is nitrogen, it exists in the atmosphere in a form which is of no particular value since neither plants (except the legumes) nor animals have the power to utilize it. Once it can be made to combine with other elements, which it does not do readily, the compounds formed can be assimilated by plants and these in turn cause other combinations to occur, finally yielding a very important group of food substances, known as proteins. Animals and men can digest these proteins and in the process promote still other combinations which ultimately form from them the important materials of our living bodies.

Nitrogen in the necessary combined form was available principally in decayed organic materials whence it could again begin the life cycle; in the deposits of saltpeter on the rainless plains of South America's west coast; and from the waste of gas works where the fossil remains of ancient forests in the form of coal are converted into more useful forms of fuel. Of all these, the deposits of saltpeter in Chile were the world's most important sources of commercially useful nitrogen. Next to them came the production of ammonia, as a by-product in the manufacture, first of illuminating gas from coal, and later of coke for our metallurgical industries.

In the preceding paragraph, the past tense is used, for on the change in that situation much of this story hinges. The amount of compound nitrogen available from gas works in the period twenty years and more ago was relatively very small and actually of about the magnitude of the world demand for it for other purposes than fertilizers. This production was widely distributed throughout the world and was definitely related to the amount of coal processed for gas manufacture. One could not afford to treat coal solely for the ammonia that might be gotten from it and consequently this source of supply was highly inflexible so far as demand for nitrogen compounds was concerned. The far larger supply from South America was in the form of nitrate whose production could be increased or decreased practically at will, depending on the demand for the product.

This greater flexibility of nitrate production in Chile

was economically offset to a large extent by the fact that it was subject to artificial control by the government and producers in Chile. A heavy export tax, which constituted the main source of revenue of this republic, was placed on nitrate, and consumers had nothing to say on the subject because there was no other comparable source of supply anywhere in the world. Besides the natural dislike which all buyers have of a monopolistic seller, the nations of the world also felt a distinct sense of insecurity on account of the Chilean control of nitrate, necessary in fertilizers, but vital to the manufacture of explosives in case of war. The possibility of effective embargoes against import of this essential raw material in war made the waging of a major conflict a decidedly hazardous undertaking for either the aggressor or the defender.

The experience of the earliest American colonists in using every means at their command to insure self-sufficiency in this respect in their conflicts with the Indians, the searching of caves where generations of bats had deposited guano, from which saltpeter might be recovered for the Confederate army in the Civil War, and the vigorous development during and immediately after the World War of the processes of making atmospheric nitrogen available in every nation to guarantee its security, evidence the seriousness of this monopoly exercised by the South American republic in times of war.

To understand the significance of this factor, it will be well to consider the following tabulation of the world's output of nitrogen in the form of its compounds during the period immediately preceding the World War:

WORLD PRODUCTION OF NITROGEN—1913

(Short tons N)

Germany	131,605
United States	39,465
Japan	3,880
France	18,945
Great Britain	99,525
Chile	476,715
Belgium	10,955
Italy	6,340
Netherlands	1,580
Norway	22,000
Russia	3,200
Canada	12,705
Poland	2,965
Yugoslavia	2,640
Sweden	4,535
Spain	3,400
Switzerland	1,825
Australia	1,245
TOTAL	843,525

Source:

By-product	306,730
Synthetic	17,965
Cyanamide	42,115
Chile	476,715

By comparing these figures with those following, which represent the same items after this gigantic conflict had forced the perfection of methods of utilizing the nitrogen of the air, and after each major nation had been at pains to secure for itself an adequate industry for the purpose, one significant result of that conflict will be apparent.

WORLD PRODUCTION OF NITROGEN—1934
(Short tons N)

Germany	462,500
United States	256,700
Japan	208,000
France	187,555
Great Britain	175,000
Chile	141,755
Belgium	109,835
Italy	98,620
Netherlands	62,905
Norway	65,505
Russia	45,000
Canada	41,080
Poland	35,165
Czechoslovakia	18,000
Yugoslavia	20,025
Sweden	8,000
Spain	8,000
Switzerland	9,465
South Africa	8,085
Hungary	3,760
Austria	1,500
British India	2,500
Australia	3,000
TOTAL	1,971,955

Source:

By-product	348,585
Synthetic	1,258,390
Cyanamide	223,225
Chile	141,755

So long as the world's chief dependence for available
nitrogen was a group of natural deposits which could be
ultimately exhausted by the heavy drain of war or even
of continued agriculture, there was always the fear that
rising costs and depletion of deposits might ultimately
seriously hamper food production in a populous world.

74

The possibility was ever present that a world famine might follow too heavy calls upon these natural resources, a calamity which has now been averted for all time by chemical industry. Had it not been for the important discoveries of chemists in this direction and their application by chemical industry, there is little question that food production would ultimately have been the limiting factor in the growth of population as Malthus had prophesied, even though the earlier discovery of artificial fertilizers had postponed its coming.

Ability to utilize the nitrogen of the air, frequently called "nitrogen fixation," is said to have been the principal weapon in the hands of Germany which induced its ruler to undertake war on such a vast scale. By 1912 Haber, a German chemist, had succeeded in producing ammonia by inducing atmospheric nitrogen to combine with hydrogen. Previously nitric acid had been made in Norway by passing air through an electric arc and in America nitrogen had been induced to combine with calcium carbide (made from coke and lime in an electric furnace) to form calcium cyanamide, directly useful as a fertilizer. But neither of these processes offered the promise of national independence that Haber's had, because both of them required relatively huge amounts of power not everywhere available. The germ of Haber's idea was to bring together nitrogen and hydrogen, both of which are normally gases, under the most favorable conditions for their combination into the presence of that touchstone of modern chemistry, a catalyst. In a way not too clearly understood, a catalyst has the power to cause chemical combinations between substances in

75

very much the same way that a broker brings buyer and seller together, and by its very presence accelerates the processes of chemical union, which might otherwise be too slow to be practical, to such a speed that results of value are achieved. Haber found that under the proper circumstances, the energy required for making ammonia from its two constituent gases was small enough to make the process economical, and the German war lords decided that, with an assured supply of combined nitrogen within their own borders to furnish them with explosives in any quantity desired, they were in a position to embark upon a war of proportions theretofore unimagined.

Nitrogen in the forms of ammonia and nitric acid has been spoken of as if the two were one and the same thing. This is not strictly correct, since the two behave very differently indeed. However, along with the development in several different countries simultaneously of the synthesis of ammonia came the perfection of previously known methods of converting it into nitric acid for the manufacture of explosives. It is obvious, therefore, that the possession of a supply of ammonia is the practical equivalent of having nitric acid or nitrates, which are readily derived from it.

As has already been indicated, the military need for compounds of nitrogen was an urgent matter during the World War. Consequently, the many national industries built to supply these essentials left the world at the close of the war with a heavy potential, if not actual, over-production for which outlets were immediately sought. Not only has the price of nitrogen in its compounds dropped precipitately under this force of selling, but a vast amount of the creative imagination of research has been expended in finding uses for these newly plentiful raw materials. Each of the advances made in this way has redounded to the benefit of the people as a whole by giving them new and better com-

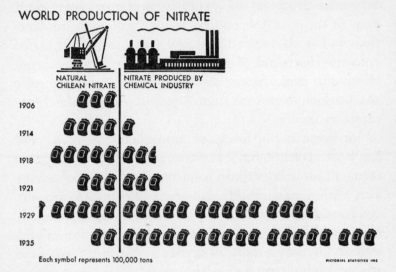

WORLD PRODUCTION OF NITRATE

NATURAL CHILEAN NITRATE   NITRATE PRODUCED BY CHEMICAL INDUSTRY

1906
1914
1918
1921
1929
1935

Each symbol represents 100,000 tons

PICTORIAL STATISTICS INC

modities, by cheapening the production of old commodities, or both.

For instance, the cost of nitrogen available for plant food in fertilizers has dropped from 14.7 cents per pound in 1910 to 6.15 cents per pound in 1933, and since the annual consumption of nitrogen in this form amounts to some 150 thousands of tons, the saving to American agriculture is of the order of 25 million dollars each year. It is not feasible to translate that amount into the reduced cost of grain, vegetables and cotton, but it is obvious that the nation's bills for these products of the farm are lowered by that amount. Neither is it feasible to calculate the effect of the freer use of nitrogenous fertilizers on the yield of American farms since numerous other factors enter the situation which would influence the result. The results of fertilization cannot be evaluated except by including in the calculation all three of the essential elements—nitrogen, potassium, and phosphorus—and even then the result is at best a guess.

In this discussion of nitrogen and its compounds emphasis has been placed on their two most important applications—fertilizers and explosives. Aside from these, there are many others of vital importance. In the preservation of food, ammonia is our principal reliance as a refrigerant for maintaining the low temperatures of our refrigerators and for the manufacture of ice. Dyes and numerous medicines also utilize various compounds of nitrogen in their manufacture. Photoengraving, which gives us the illustrations in books and other printed matter, consumes large quantities of nitric acid in etching its designs on metal for reproduction. A recent use for synthetic ammonia, now so abundantly and cheaply available, is as a medium for the transportation of the hydrogen it contains. Because of its inherent properties, hydrogen is difficult to transport from place to place economically, but ammonia can be carried about in tank-cars. Where hydrogen is required, as in the hardening of fats, it is now customary to buy synthetic ammonia, and when it is received at the point of use, simply reverse the process of its manufacture to get back the desired hydrogen and waste the nitrogen.

This anomalous situation has resulted from the extreme present cheapness of the synthetic process of producing ammonia. One might continue indefinitely describing the values obtained from nitrogen and its compounds, but it should be quite obvious from what has been said that it is vital to our civilization.

POTASSIUM

Equally important in the trinity of fertilizing elements, potassium has been principally derived from the working of chemical salt deposits laid down by prehistoric oceans which have evaporated so slowly as to allow the various salts contained in them to deposit in separate layers or strata. The process of forming beds of different kinds of salts in separate layers by the evaporation of the sea water containing them is now going on around the Dead Sea in Palestine; and in this one spot in the world it is possible to observe both the formation of these salt beds and their utilization by the chemical industry. In the geological past, seas which covered parts of Germany and Alsace, Texas and New Mexico and several other parts of the world undoubtedly became landlocked in much the same way that the Dead Sea has, and the slow process of evaporation through the ages allowed the salts dissolved in the water on its course to the sea to deposit in layers, each containing in more or less pure form one or more of the many salts originally in the water. In more recent times, the same thing has occurred in the desert sections of southern California and Nevada, leaving semi-liquid lakes, which are actually vast deposits of salts contain-

79

ing more or less salt water. It is unnecessary here to go into detail of the method of accumulation of these vast deposits of salts left by evaporating seas beyond the general statement that those parts of the earth and its rocks which can be dissolved by water ultimately find their way to the sea and that among these, the most plentiful are compounds of sodium (principally sodium chloride, familiar as the salt on the table), potassium, calcium and magnesium, together with a number of others of lesser present consequence. The evaporation of the water tends to concentrate these salts to the point where the remaining water will hold no more of them and immediately they form more or less pure deposits of crystals. Naturally, this process is progressive and those salts which are least soluble come out first, to be followed by others in the order of their increasing solubility or of their decreasing plenitude. In this way, beds of relatively pure salts of potassium have been formed and can be mined for use.

Because the natural salts of potassium are not those most desired, and also because the process of their deposition has been influenced in its course by many factors, the crude product as mined has had to undergo various processes of chemical manufacture to refine them and put them into the most desirable forms for use. In fertilizer, the preferred forms are potassium chloride (muriate of potash), mined directly from some deposits without further refining and prepared from others by processes of crystallization; potassium sulfate, similarly obtained naturally or by recrystallization; potassium nitrate and, latterly, potassium phosphate, the last two made especially for inclusion in modern concentrated fertilizers.

These natural deposits of potassium salts were discovered by geologists but they depend upon the processes of chemical industry to make them valuable. Because they are found in fixed localities, each under more or less strict national control, other nations have in time of stringent need, on account of shipping embargoes and other causes, sought diligently for other possible supplies within their own borders, sometimes with success. The earliest source of potash (potassium carbonate), the one as a matter of fact from which the word itself comes, was the leachings of ashes from the wood fires heating pots. These supplied our primitive forebears with their most common alkali which they used in the manufacture of soap from the drippings of fat from their kitchens. Indeed, consideration of this source of potassium salts led to the conclusion that they were essential to the growth of plants since all plant ashes contained substantial amounts of this element. Even the giant kelps and seaweeds which grow in the ocean are able to absorb potassium compounds freely and reject the almost identical sodium compounds which exist in the water of the oceans in concentrations nearly a hundred-fold greater. The slops of distilleries contain recoverable amounts of potash. Many rocks contain varying percentages of potash and some of these can, under stress, be utilized as sources of its supply (notably alunite, wyomingite and some of the feldspars). Numerous other rocks and minerals contain smaller amounts of potassium compounds which can be made available profitably only as an incident to some other operation. Recently, by the application of a new technic to the recovery of fumes and dust from cement mills, substantial amounts of potash concentrates have been made available from this source at prices which make their present recovery and use economically sound. In 1935, the United States produced 189,800 tons of potassium salts (as K_2O) and imported 213,104 tons. The greater part of this was used in fertilizing American farms.

Chemical industry enters the potash picture principally as a refiner of Nature's products, to separate from them unwanted materials and to render them adaptable to man's needs. It is pertinent to point out that in the refining operation the other material separated in the process becomes what are commonly called by the much misunderstood term, by-products. Thus borax, salt, soda, Epsom salt (magnesium sulfate) and numerous others are simultaneously produced in refining naturally occurring mixtures to obtain their potash content. One may differentiate between the primary products of an operation, its by-products and its wastes. Those materials constituting its main objective and salable for a price to pay for the process are properly primary products. By-products are other materials whose total value, either through price per unit or quantity made, is too small to be regularly harnessed with the support of the operation. Wastes have a value too small to permit of any profitable disposition. It is thus obvious that the vagaries of supply and demand and the economics of manufacture may, from time to time, shift any product from one classification to another and back again.

PHOSPHORUS

Phosphorus is useful for many purposes. Most striking of these are matches which consume many tons annually and screening smokes and incendiary bombs in war, but its principal value lies in the application of its compounds in fertilizing our fields to promote the growth of foodstuffs. For this purpose, it is equally essential with nitrogen and potassium. Like them it requires chemical treatment of a naturally occurring raw material to make it available for plant food. In nature, phosphorus is most plentiful in the form of phosphate rock, tricalcium phosphate, which occurs in great beds in South Carolina, Tennessee, in the northwestern United States and in northern Africa as a layer in limestone, and as pebbles in Florida, where it is mined by dredging from the bottoms of streams and dug out of deposits left by streams now dry. It is presumed that these naturally occurring phosphate beds were at one time in their existence the bones of prehistoric animals and coral polyps from which the slow process of ages has separated this important ingredient and concentrated it under conditions favorable for its deposition.

In its naturally occurring form, phosphorus in phosphate rock is relatively insoluble in the water of the soil and is too slowly available to plants to be successful as a fertilizing material. However, when the native rock is ground and treated with sulfuric acid in proper amount, the insoluble compound is converted into a form readily assimilated by the roots of plants. This operation, by which is produced the superphosphate of commerce, consumes large quantities of sulfuric acid, so great a proportion of the whole output, indeed, that it is this use which controls (if anything can be said to do so) the demand for and hence the price of this important acid.

Superphosphate prepared by the simple action of sulfuric acid on phosphate rock consists of a mixture of the acid phosphates of calcium with a considerable amount of calcium sulfate. This latter material is familiar in the form of native gypsum (from which plaster of Paris and many valuable building materials are made) and in the fertilizer it serves the same purpose that gypsum does when applied, as it often is, as land plaster. Not only does this material have a beneficial effect on certain soils but at the same time it serves as a useful diluent for the active fertilizing constituents of the mixture as used.

While the gypsum of superphosphate is often of value, the weight which it adds to the mixed fertilizer so increases freight charges over long distances that efforts have been made to avoid producing it in making phosphorus available to plants. Several methods have been proposed for making a concentrated phosphoric acid direct from the rock and using this to replace sulfuric acid in treating other quantities of raw material. While none of these has yet attained anything approaching the importance of the sulfuric acid treatment, yet the possibility they offer of increasing the concentration of available plant food in fertilizers has been so far proved as to encourage further developments along this line.

By merely treating phosphate rock with large amounts of sulfuric acid of high concentration, the phosphoric acid can be set free and separated from the calcium sulfate simultaneously formed. The strong phosphoric acid can then be used to treat raw phosphate rock to produce a superphosphate of high concentration. Other methods have been developed for producing strong phosphoric acid which are based on the use of extremely high temperatures to cause a chemical reaction between phosphate rock and common quartz sand. So high is the temperature used—it may be produced in furnaces heated either by fuel or by electricity—that the phosphorus pentoxide from the melt actually boils out and can be collected with water or dilute acid to form a concentrated phosphoric acid. These methods of preparing concentrated phosphoric acid have made possible the growing number of concentrated fertilizers now available to farmers. While the older method of direct treatment of rock phosphate with sulfuric acid yielded a superphosphate of 15 to 17 per cent available plant food, the substitution of phosphoric acid produces a material containing nearly three times as much. Since both the nitrogen and the potassium required in the finished fertilizer are available in concentrated forms, the "triple" superphosphate thus obtained permits the preparation of mixtures in which 40 to 50 per cent is actual useful matter as contrasted to 16 to 20 per cent, which is the average with sulfuric-acid-produced superphosphate. The implications of this improvement, still not fully developed, have to do with the greater economies in fertilizer manufacture since lower freight costs will allow centralized production in larger units than the scattered small plants that have characterized the fertilizer industry in the past.

The newer methods of recovering phosphoric acid from native rock have had important implications in other directions as well as in the fertilizer industry. While industry's main reliance for acid requirements had previously included sulfuric, hydrochloric and nitric acids, phosphoric acid has assumed a place of new prominence in the industrial world.

MIXED FERTILIZERS

The three constituents of a complete fertilizer which we have been discussing are those most commonly required by average soils to maintain their fertility. Numerous other constituents—iron, magnesium, manganese, sulfur and others—have been discovered from time to time to affect favorably the yields or qualities of various crops in various localities. From time to time, these minor elements have been unduly stressed as have one or other of the three major constituents. Each of the three elements—nitrogen, potassium and phosphorus—is essential to the average soil for which commercial mixed fertilizers are prepared. The omission or increase in quantity of any constituent should be undertaken only after careful chemical and agronomical examination of the soil and consideration of the crop.

Commercial fertilizers consist of three to five hundred pounds of available plant food diluted or extended with harmless inert materials to make a ton of product ready to be spread on the field. The mixing and diluting operations are necessary to enable the farmer safely to apply the product to his crops without danger of injuring them. One may compare the treatment of a field with commercial fertilizer to salting one's food. If too much salt is applied, the effect is unpleasant and if carried too far may be actually dangerous to one's digestion. In the same way, too great doses of fertilizer may injure growing plants, although proper amounts will greatly benefit them.

The economic disadvantage of handling a ton of material to apply only a few hundred pounds of plant food to the soil is obvious. Efforts have been made during recent years to avoid this added expense by supplying to the farmer the most concentrated plant food available, together with instructions in the proper method of dilution and subsequent handling to prevent injury to crops. Formerly, the most dilute constituent of a fertilizer mixture, and hence the limit to concentration, was the superphosphate of which the average ton contained less than 350 pounds of active, available phosphoric acid. This fact, among others, prevented realizing the obvious economies to be had by handling concentrated materials. However, with the perfection of the newer methods of making this essential available in concentrated form, this obstacle has been removed. There are now commercially available fertilizers containing as much as 1000 pounds of actual plant food per ton. The technic of using these in the fields must be understood better and more generally before they are universally used.

The exact evaluation of the increased yield in food-stuffs produced by the application of commercial fertilizers is quite impossible, since no one has been to the trouble to learn the difference in the yield of every field with and without this added assistance, and, even if it were possible to persuade the farmers to perform this gigantic experiment, the uncontrollable vagaries of season and weather might entirely vitiate the result.

The total amount of commercial, as distinct from natural, fertilizer consumed in the United States in 1933 was valued at $82,810,953.

The cost of the additional yield of our farms may be said to have been the cost of the fertilizer used in their production, which is only a small proportion of their market value. The difference is a substantial item in the profit to the country realized from the activities of its chemical industry.

PROTECTION OF GROWING PLANTS

Locusts, aphids, boll-weevils and other insects feed upon growing plants and thus prevent their proper production of food and clothing for the human race. In addition to insects, innumerable varieties of fungi destroy growing vegetation. Against them, the only successful weapons of attack are products of chemical industry. Compounds of arsenic, fluorine, lead, copper, and mercury and various mixtures containing oils, lime, sulfur, nicotine, pyrethrum, and others when sprayed

or dusted on the growing plants leave films of poisonous residues which kill the insects or destroy the fungus.
Cotton, corn, wheat, many fruits and vegetables, and,
indeed, practically all food plants must be saved from
destruction by the use of these agricultural fungicides
and insecticides. New weapons and methods are being
constantly sought to make pest destruction easier, safer
and more complete. Recently added to our potent insecticides is rotenone, extracted from the root of the
cubé or derris plant. It is remarkable in being deadly
to insects, but relatively innocuous to men and higher
animals, an extremely desirable characteristic. Other
methods depend upon applying non-toxic materials to
plants to cause them to generate in their own sap substances which kill sucking insects. Research chemists,
cooperating with chemical manufacturers, are actively
investigating to learn why particular materials are effective and to make them more so.

In this continuing war on insect pests, every strata-
gem possible is being employed. Careful study of insect
life reveals that one of their most vulnerable points is
the peculiarity of their breathing apparatus. Indeed,
the fact that Nature failed to provide them with lungs,
but rather distributed their breathing apparatus over
the whole surface of their bodies, has been shown to be
the limiting factor in the growth of insects. As their
bulk increases, the surface of their bodies shrinks in relation to their volume and the largest species are weak
because of their inability to breathe enough air. This
provides an especially vulnerable point of attack and
many insecticides are designed to stimulate breathing

to permit the introduction of poisons in this way. The intricacy of the methods employed and the effectiveness of their results is a story filled with wonder.

PRESERVATION OF FOOD

Chemical industry does not abandon the task of insuring an adequate food supply after it has made more bountiful the yield of our fields, but rather its beneficent influence continues throughout the life of the planted crops in the field and even to the table of the ultimate consumer. In this journey, numerous agencies are in wait to pounce upon and destroy foodstuffs before they can serve their ultimate purpose. Insect and fungus pests attack growing crops; bacteria and other destructive agencies prey upon the harvested food to render it unsuited or unavailable for human use; and countless other hazards must be avoided or overcome before the farmer's product is set upon the table. In all of these protective measures, the products of chemical industry are potent weapons against the enemies of men.

Even before seed is planted it is subject to attack by various organisms which would sap its vitality and prevent it from yielding a healthy plant. Since healthy fertile seeds are essential to bountiful crops, chemical products are first used in this way in protecting our food supply. Certain recently discovered compounds of mercury and of copper, similar in some respects to the mercurochrome of the family medicine shelf and like it closely related to the dyes which give color to our clothing, have a rather remarkable ability to make the

lives of parasites on seeds highly uncomfortable without destroying the vitality of the seed. By wetting or dusting seeds with these disinfectants a very small quantity remains on them and the attack of fungi is prevented. Sulfuric acid has been similarly used with success. Several other common disinfectants have this ability to a substantial extent, but none is so effective as these newly devised organic compounds of mercury and copper which permanently protect the seed without in any way affecting its vitality. Bulbs are similarly protected by treatment with gaseous carbon tetrachloride and other chemical agents.

Substances of the same general character have been found extraordinarily effective in preventing the destruction of fish nets by numerous micro-organisms which live on the string of which the net is composed. These particular compounds have the remarkable ability of attaching themselves intimately to the fibers of the net in much the same way that a dye might and thus make the fiber permanently poisonous to micro-organisms. Salt brines are even more widely used to preserve nets and keep them free from destructive matter. The saving to our fisheries through the general use of such protective measures will ultimately reach an annual total of many millions of dollars, which by that amount will reduce the cost of catching the fish which form so large a part of our national dietary. In similar ways fish lines can be preserved from premature decay and made practically immune to rotting.

In the storage of seed and grain of all kinds, even when processed, numerous insects present a constant danger of loss and it is necessary to destroy them before they can consume the grain and prevent it from reaching the human race. Numerous fumigants are thus used for killing insects and their eggs before they destroy necessary foods. Among these is hydrocyanic acid (prussic acid), one of our most potent poisons. The grain elevator, or other closed space containing the grain, is filled with the vapors of hydrocyanic acid, closed for a satisfactory period of time, and finally opened and completely ventilated to remove the poisonous gas. This treatment kills all living and breathing things. Because of the hazards of hydrocyanic acid to persons, chemical industry has provided other, safer insecticides for this use which have the peculiar property of killing insects and their eggs without harming human beings who, through accident or design, breathe their vapors. Among these newer insecticides used in granaries are carbon bisulfide, ethylene oxide and methyl formate, synthetic materials without counterparts in nature. These are mixed with carbon dioxide in either the liquid or solid form (dry ice) and allowed to evaporate into the enclosed space. The vapors destroy pests, but only prolonged exposure causes anything more than a passing discomfort to a person.

Our annual losses of grains through the depredation of insects in stored grain and flour have been greater than $300,000,000. The cost of the fumigants supplied by the chemical industry for the purpose has amounted to only a fraction of 1 per cent of this amount. The more general use of fumigants in this way will still further increase the profit from them even though it is unlikely that they will ever completely wipe out our loss of foodstuffs through the ravages of insects.

Not only are our vegetable foods ravaged by insects, but a huge toll is exacted from our supply of animal foods by diseases spread by insects. The various insect parasites of swine, cattle and sheep not only sap the vitality of their hosts, but carry with them, from one animal to another, many virulent diseases which decimate herds and flocks. In this phase of our war on insects, chemical industry also supplies essential weapons in the form of insecticides adapted to these applications, antiseptics to limit the spread of disease germs and various serums and vaccines to prevent and to cure the diseases they cause. Here, too, the annual cost of remedial and preventive agents ($4,382,000) is insignificant, compared with the reduction in loss of stock.

It is impossible accurately to evaluate the saving effected by our use of insecticides, since this may in the extreme case amount to as much as 100 per cent of the crop. The total cost to the United States of the ravages of insects is approximately $2,000,000,000 per annum. This amounts to approximately $17.00 per person per year, and this cost is higher for the average family than the cost of electricity. It has been estimated that the loss of fruit through the ravages of insects adds 25 per cent to the cost of fruit to the consumer. In other words an apple which sells for 5 cents might be sold with as great profit at 4 cents if no insects infested apple trees. When one considers that without the protection afforded by products of the chemical industry our crops might be entirely destroyed by insects, the value of this protection becomes evident.

After the crop has been harvested, chemical industry aids in conserving our supply of food by its preservation from points of plentiful excess to places and seasons of relative scarcity. Most important in this respect is the supply of materials used in producing refrigeration. Among these, ammonia, now made synthetically as described above in connection with fertilizers, carbon dioxide, sulfur dioxide, methyl chloride, ethyl chloride, isobutane, propane, organic fluorine compounds and numerous others are the working fluids in the ordinary refrigerating machines, producing ice or direct cold. Frozen brines as methods of distributing cold are widely used. Solid carbon dioxide, best known as dry ice, is a comparatively recent addition to our means of applying cold. It is a by-product of several important manufacturing operations, as well as a direct product of others.

Cold, thus produced, is capable of preventing change in perishable foodstuffs without preservatives. The value of the cold produced by artificial refrigeration, most of which is applied to the saving of foodstuffs in cold-storage warehouses, in processing factories and in homes, reaches the extraordinary total of approximately 1825 millions of dollars annually, yet the value of the products of chemical industry used for the purpose does not exceed an estimated total of some 2.5 millions of dollars annually.

Canning of foods is more and more utilizing help supplied through the products of chemical manufacture to make it a still safer way of storing foods until needed. The tinning of sheet iron used in making cans consumes huge quantities of sulfuric acid. A special rubber compound is used in the fabrication of rolled-seam cans to insure the permanent tightness of their joints without the use of solder, and every one is familiar with the rubber sealing rings chemical industry produces to seal the covers on glass jars, which are, themselves, products of this industry. Paraffin wax, produced from petroleum, provides a valuable seal for preserves and jellies. Soldered cans are put together with solder and flux, both products of chemical manufacture. Recently, chemical industry has developed several lacquers for coating the metal of cans to avoid the use of plating with tin, the customary preventive of corrosion by air and by the material packed in them. This improvement is expected, when fully utilized, to aid in freeing this country from dependence on foreign-controlled sources of metallic tin.

In other processes of food preservation, smoking, salting, brining, corning, drying and quick-freezing, the chemical industry supplies necessary raw materials to the operations of the food conserver.

Chemical processes are practiced in many parts of the food industry in the preparation of foodstuffs and in the manufacture of industrially valuable materials from the products of the farm. Refineries treat the juices of cane and sugar beets to recover the purest of common chemical compounds, sugar, for human consumption. In its processes numerous chemical products are employed—lime, active carbons, sulfur dioxide and various filter aids—to insure the purity of the product. Molasses, a by-product of sugar-refining, is the basic raw material of the alcohol industry and together with corn and other grains supplies numerous important solvents. Corn, subjected to mechanical and chemical treatment, also yields starch, dextrin, a number of other adhesives, and the valuable corn-sugar (glucose), as well as oils, feeds and other valuable products. In addition to these important industries engaged in the chemical treatment of farm products, a number of significant materials are being made from many agricultural wastes in many plants employing methods new within a decade. The hulls of oats yield furfural, a valuable starting point for chemical synthesis; waste sugar cane, from which the sugar has been extracted, forms the raw material for making useful wall-board and insulation; sawmill wastes are being formed into building materials; corn unfit for other use is fermented to yield important solvents, butanol and acetone, of value in the manufacture of nitrocellulose lacquers; and the waste skimmed milk of creameries is treated to produce milk sugar, casein (base of adhesives, plastics and paper coatings and now used as the raw material for making a "synthetic wool" in Italy), and other valuable by-products of dairy industry. Development in the chemical utilization of farm products has been particularly rapid in recent years and much may be expected from it.

Related to the food industry is the production of a wide variety of adhesives of great value in industry. Wastes of packing houses and fishing yield glue and

97

gelatin; skimmed milk and soy-bean meal are sources of casein glues; starchy vegetables, notably corn and potatoes, supply dextrins and other modified starches of valuable adhesive properties; rubber latex and solutions of rubber in appropriate solvents cement surfaces together; natural resins (rosin, shellac and damar) and several synthetic resins and compounds provide valuable additions to our variety of cementing materials; and even liquid glass (silicate of soda) is valuable in holding our packages together. Although derived from widely different raw materials and having similarly various abilities and applications, each of these chemical products materially assists in holding things together.

5.

Wheels and Wings

UNLIKE most other human activities, methods of transportation have survived the evolutionary process to such an extent that even today, when the swift flight of airplanes transports man and his burdens over whole continents in a very few hours, the crudest early means of transport are somewhere still essential. The most rapidly progressing system is to be found in the United States, where relatively huge distances make transportation the fundamental cement which unites a vast population spread over an immense territory into a single political unit. With this primary cause acting as a spur to inventive genius, the arts of communication and transportation have developed in this country

99

to a point scarcely imaginable elsewhere in the world, and in these particular fields the American people have laid the rest of the world deeply in their debt. Without in the least detracting from other important contributions to this phenomenal development, chemical industry can claim and boast of its important help in this progress.

The cruder means of transportation, by wooden ships propelled by the wind, by pack horse and by ox cart, can scarcely be considered part of this picture, so far back in the remote past do their beginnings and perfection lie. As soon as means of travel involving the wheel are considered, however it may be utilized, there immediately come into range chemical operations which add to the convenience and efficiency of transport. The crude wooden wheel of the ancient ox cart, untired and unlubricated, was no match in its slow, creaking progress for the great distances commerce required to be covered on the American continent. Scarcely better were the lumbering rafts laboriously poled along rivers or the barges drawn by mules, horses or men along our early canals. Yet, in spite of their extreme crudity, each of these has survived the inroads of more convenient and rapid carriers because of some innate vitality which has made it ideally suited for particular purposes. Much that was picturesque in the early development of this continent has vanished with the replacement of these crudities, but the tradition continues even today in the often heroic reliability of their successors.

Although the art of building roads was developed to

early perfection by the Romans in their conquering march over the then known world, and their methods are still the fundamental principles of engineering utilized today in the construction of highways, they were unable to perfect their creations for lack of materials now essential to the increasing swiftness of travel. They, too, adopted the wheel from the lore of a past even then lost in the dim mists of antiquity. It is doubtful, however, whether they had reached the point of lubricating bearings to preserve the wheel and to lighten the load on animal motive power. It is fairly certain that the application of a metal tire to protect the wheel's wooden rim from the wear of the road was considered by them important only to war chariots, rather than to the lumbering carts of commerce. In these two important particulars, chemical industry and its twin, metallurgy, have materially increased efficiency by raising the allowable load for a given power through lubrication and by lengthening the life of the vehicle by supplying tires of greater resistance to wear.

The use of vehicles required improved roads over which to travel, and these were supplied by following the crowned design and deep-laid foundation of the ancient Romans with a surface developed by the Scotchman, MacAdam, consisting of a suitable mixture of broken rock assorted as to size from coarse chunks to fine sandy particles. Over roads of this character, horse-drawn vehicles with steel-tired wheels could travel at the highest speeds attainable by animals with reasonable efficiency and satisfaction. Two innovations in the motive power of transport required improved highways; the steam-driven locomotive on its steel wheels and the gasoline-powered automobile which travelled on pneumatic tires of rubber.

Steel wheels could not be satisfactorily carried on any but a steel road. Through the earliest rails, which were no more than thin strips of wrought iron as a protection over wooden tracks, the development progresses to the modern alloy steel rails and wheels of corresponding properties, over which loads literally hundreds of times greater than any contemplated in the beginning are safely and swiftly carried from end to end of the country and into almost every hamlet. The story of steel is so closely bound with the development of chemical manufacture that it is necessary to consider it in some detail here. Not only has the chemical development of steel been essentially important in rail transportation, but it has fundamentally affected so many other human activities as to be well nigh the basic development of our times.

Iron is most commonly found in the form of its oxides—compounds of metallic iron with oxygen—which are yellow, red, brown or black minerals widely distributed in nature. To obtain the metal, it is necessary to break up this combination. This is most easily done by heating the ore in the presence of some other substance which forms a more stable combination with its oxygen than iron does. Charcoal and coke, both forms of carbon, are the cheapest and most easily available materials of this sort, and when heated with iron ore readily release the metal. Other materials ordinarily present in the ore must also be removed, an operation commonly accomplished by adding limestone to the mixture to form fusible compounds with the impurities present. Metallic iron, when molten, has the ability to dissolve carbon much as water dissolves sugar, so that the product of the blast furnace (called pig iron) is actually iron containing large amounts of carbon dissolved in it. Some of this carbon separates as the iron solidifies. When refined and cast, pig iron is known as cast iron. Cast iron has great strength, but the separated carbon makes it too brittle for many purposes. Iron having the carbon burned out of it and further purified is commercially known as wrought iron and possesses qualities of value in many ways. The addition to it of precise amounts of carbon makes it more generally useful in the form of steel. Even this plain carbon steel, universally used in all manner of construction, is not ideally adapted to every purpose, and investigations have revealed that the addition to it of more or less small amounts of other metals and materials which dissolve in or combine with it alters its qualities in many desirable ways. Thus, while steel has a very high elasticity as compared with other metals and materials, the addition of proper amounts of silicon with manganese and chromium with vanadium to it yields springs which are practically unbreakable in ordinary use. Manganese added to steel as a purifier also gives it a toughness which resists abrasion and shock. In the making of tools for working metals, tungsten, molybdenum, chromium, cobalt and titanium are among the alloying ingredients which allow tools to cut faster and at higher temperatures without losing their temper. The field of ferro alloys, by which are meant the combinations of iron or steel with other metals and elements, is almost infinitely broad and of signal service to man.

The early application of steel as the roadway for the iron horse was successful to a degree, and as the power and weight of our steam-driven vehicles became greater and greater in the course of their evolution, steels had to be constantly improved to keep ahead of the demands made upon them, both as rails and as other parts of the railroad system. Later, as other methods of transportation, particularly the gasoline automobile, developed, new alloys necessary to meet their special requirements were forthcoming and these, in turn, have had important consequences for the railroads.

Despite dependence on metals as prime materials of construction, our vast railroad systems utilize huge quantities of timber as well, and to an equal degree our forests contribute to water-borne transportation. Yet wood is seldom ideally adapted to these purposes without further treatment by products of chemical industry.

Wood, one of the most adaptable of structural materials, is subject to deterioration like all other structural materials. Fungi, insects, and marine borers are the principal agents of destruction of wood. When it is considered that estimates place the annual loss of wood due to decay at one-fifth of the annual cut, and that 45 million dollars' worth of damage is caused yearly by insects besides the many millions more caused by marine borers, it is clear why even in early times the need for the treatment of wood to prevent deterioration was thoroughly appreciated. Frequent references in Pliny's

writings to the need for treatment of wood and vegetable fibers to prevent destruction were amply justified
even then. Subsequent service records for coal-tar
creosote, coal tar, creosote-coal tar solutions, creosote-
petroleum mixtures, and zinc chloride injected into
wood by standard wood preserving processes have
proved their value.

In the early history of the United States it was possible to select certain durable woods for the specific
uses where this durability was needed most. This large
demand rapidly depleted the supply of naturally durable woods and the cry of famine was heard. Railroads
are the past and present largest single user of treated
wood products. White oak was a widely used tie material which had to be purchased at a premium. The
necessity for the treatment and utilization of non-durable woods became increasingly apparent with the exhaustion of this wood. Pine, red oak, gum, and other
non-durable woods can be converted to highly satisfactory tie materials with an average lengthening of the
life span by five times by preservative treatment. A
conservative estimate based on the cost of treated ties,
the equivalent necessary number of untreated ties, replacement costs, interest rates, etc., places the average
saving from the use of each treated cross tie at the
round figure of three dollars. The railroads purchased
some 75,000,000 treated cross ties in 1927. Add to this
the saving realized by the treatment of other wood
products, such as switch ties, poles, piles and lumber,
and the annual saving assumes large proportions.
Equally striking is the resulting conservation of our

forests. It has been estimated there are 50,000,000 acres of forest area in existence at this time due to the preservative treatment of wood. It also is estimated that at the present time the saving of forested area per year by this industry is about 4,000,000 acres.

In addition to materials of construction and the lubrication of bearings in railroad transportation, chemical industry has contributed materials of value in the lighting and signalling systems which make rail transport safe and others of importance in making rail journeys comfortable. Among the most recent of these has been the structural use of light alloys of aluminum and stainless steels to accelerate movement of persons and goods, and the increasing use of methods of air conditioning to add to the comfort of travel through unpleasant weather. Both of these important improvements have been adapted to railroad equipment from their original development for other purposes, pressure being applied from outside to force improvements here.

The development of automotive transportation has had a most far-reaching effect in the creation of new products through chemical industry and in fostering the utilization of existing resources in many new ways. The popularity of gasoline-powered vehicles was dependent on the invention of the pneumatic rubber tire for the early safety bicycles and its adaptation to the carrying of the heavier loads of larger vehicles. Although early automobiles were mounted on wheels whose tires were of solid rubber, like those of horse-drawn buggies of the same period, these were ill adapted to the higher speeds made possible by the me-

chanical power of the internal combustion engine and consequently the improvement of the bicycle tire to fit it to automobile service was necessary to give the new vehicles a real start in the world. The first effects of this were evident in the industry compounding rubber, which of itself is a story worth the telling, but more particularly did it reveal the inadequacy of the road surfaces which had previously served so well for slower horse-drawn vehicles.

The broader bearing of pneumatic tires on the road surface, coupled with the greater speed of travel, had the immediate effect of drawing out of the macadam surface the fine particles which serve as the bond to hold the whole together. This required immediate attention to road surfaces and the addition of other binders to prevent their complete destruction by automobile traffic. Among the earliest of these were the residual tarry oils left from the distillation of petroleum and coal tar which prevented dust from being drawn out of the road surface to fly about the countryside. As demands on the roads became more and more severe, heavier asphalts were applied both as a binder and as a surface coating. These, like the earlier road oils, could be obtained from the refining of certain petroleum oils and were also secured from natural lakes of bitumen in the island of Trinidad and elsewhere, both products of chemical refining operations. Later, calcium chloride, a by-product made cheaply in vast quantities in the manufacture of soda by the Solvay process, and common salt were widely used on roadways to lay the dust through their property of absorbing moisture from the air to bind the surface. The next step of real consequence in road building was the general adoption of concrete as a road-building material for those arteries carrying heavy traffic. Previously, concrete had been applied in numerous structures, but the extended surface of thousands of miles of roadway and the severe conditions of wear and weather to which it is exposed presented new problems to the cement industry, both in the manufacture of its product and in the method of application. The solutions of these problems, all involving important chemical developments, have been of great significance both to the industry and to the users of concrete structures, for they have shown the way toward modification of cement's properties to meet particular needs. One has but to consider the fact that the huge Boulder Dam in the Colorado River necessitated the manufacture of a special cement to permit its construction as a virtually monolithic block of concrete, to realize how far the art of manufacturing cement has progressed beyond the relatively simpler material of the pre-automotive age. In this particular construction, it was necessary to provide a cement which would generate a minimum amount of heat during hardening, since such a mass of the usual type of cement would have become so hot inside during the setting process that it would have cracked badly as it cooled. This was achieved by the application of the same type of study that yielded a satisfactory cement for road surfacing, and, like it, was a product of chemical transformation of a mixture of natural rocks in the proper proportions with other supplementary materials added to give the finished cement the precise properties desired.

The automobile, as it traverses the millions of miles of highways of our country carrying men and their goods where they would be, has been described as a virtual chemical factory on wheels, for its fundamental driving force is a chemical reaction between gasoline vapor and air conducted under precise conditions of control. It may quite as truly be described as a product, from roadway to top, from tail light to bumper, of chemical industry, since so many of the materials of which it is made are produced by processes of chemical change of Nature's raw materials. In order to make this discussion follow a logical sequence, it will be necessary to dissect a modern automobile into several parts and examine each of these closely to determine its origins. It will be be virtually impossible to recognize in any of the parts the natural sources from which they came, so dissimilar have they become in the processes of chemical elaboration and refinement. For convenience, we may carry out our dissection in such a way as to separate the tires, the fuel, the metal structure and the many appurtenances which go to make a comfortable and efficient vehicle of an internal combustion engine mounted on wheels. By following these convenient sub-divisions, the many implications and ramifications of the automobile industry will be more easily unified.

Authorities are in reasonable agreement that the automobile resulted from the development of the pneumatic tire rather than that the pressure put upon the refiners of kerosene to dispose of the gasoline, which previously had made their product dangerously explosive, was the ruling cause of our modern crowded highways. It is not particularly germane to the present discussion which of these two facts was of more importance. Rather than become involved in fruitless argument, it will be better to relate the histories of both, since both are intimately bound up in the contribution chemical industry has made to this method of transportation.

The connection of chemical history with rubber actually began with the discovery in 1839 by Charles Goodyear that the heating of a mixture of rubber and sulfur yielded an elastic material which would no longer soften and become sticky when warmed. This chemical reaction, later known as vulcanization, was the key which unlocked the myriad potentialities of rubber giving the world a new material whose value in our modern civilization is beyond estimate.

By varying the amount of sulfur in the mixture and the time and temperature at which it was heated, a variety of different materials could be made from these same ingredients. Soft, flexible rubber usually contains not more than three per cent sulfur, while completely vulcanized hard rubber contains about 32 per cent sulfur.

Goodyear's discovery of the vulcanization reaction had been made with a mixture which also contained white lead. It was soon found that this, or similar materials such as litharge, increased the rate of reaction between the sulfur and rubber and made it possible to complete the vulcanization in a shorter time or at a lower temperature. These materials were used as "accelerators" until about 1906 when it was found that small amounts of various organic chemicals also acted as very powerful accelerators. Although several hundred different accelerators of this type have been discovered the number in wide commercial use is less than twenty. These organic materials are so powerful that they reduce the time required for vulcanization to one tenth or even one twentieth of that required without them. Some of these accelerators are sufficiently powerful to cause the vulcanization to take place at room temperature, although practically all of the accelerators in commercial use are not active at temperatures below 220° F. These accelerators have not only resulted in savings due to the reduced time required for vulcanization but they have also improved the quality of the vulcanized rubber produced.

The chemical constitution of these accelerators is usually complex. Typical materials in this class are: diphenyl-guanidine; butyraldehyde-aniline; mercapto-benzo-thiazole.

Rubber chemists have discovered other materials which improve the quality of rubber goods. Various pigments, especially carbon black, which results from burning natural gas with a quantity of air insufficient for its complete combustion, reinforce rubber and increase its strength and especially its resistance to abrasion. As a result, large quantities of carbon black are now used in all tire treads.

Another group of complex organic chemicals have

been discovered which greatly reduce the deterioration of rubber on aging. These materials which began to be used in increasing amounts about 1925 have made a very large improvement in the wearing qualities of all types of rubber goods. Deterioration in storage or from oxidation during use has now been greatly reduced.

While all types of rubber goods have been improved by the discovery of improved chemicals, the greatest savings have been made in the tire industry for about 80 per cent of all the rubber used in the United States goes into tires and tubes.

The quality of automobile tires has shown an astounding improvement. Every one whose motoring experience extends back ten or fifteen years can recall the frequency with which flat tires interrupted even a short journey. Total tire mileage was low and uncertain. It is conservatively estimated that average tire mileage in the United States has increased as follows:

Year	Average Mileage
1906	4,000
1910	5,000
1914	6,000
1918	7,200
1922	8,600
1926	10,300
1930	12,500
1934	15,000

At the same time the cost of tires has also been reduced, partly due to reduced cost of raw materials,

113

partly to improved manufacturing methods, and partly to the discovery and use of more effective chemicals.

The improvements in quality and reductions in cost have combined to reduce tire costs per mile steadily until they are now only about one-fifth of the cost in 1918. The resultant savings to the American people have been so large that they are hard to believe until

AVERAGE MILEAGE AND COST PER TIRE

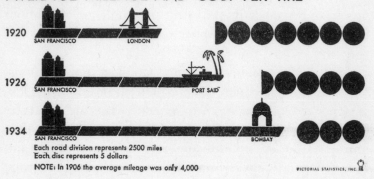

1920   SAN FRANCISCO   LONDON

1926   SAN FRANCISCO   PORT SAID

1934   SAN FRANCISCO   BOMBAY

Each road division represents 2500 miles
Each disc represents 5 dollars
NOTE: In 1906 the average mileage was only 4,000

PICTORIAL STATISTICS, INC.

the detailed calculations are examined. These are shown in the following table. The second column shows the estimated tire cost per 10,000 miles of driving for the fifteen years ending in 1934. The third column shows the calculated savings per car in each year, representing the difference between the actual amounts paid for tires and tubes, and the amounts which would have been paid if tire quality and price had remained at 1920 levels. The fourth column shows the vehicle registration in millions. Assuming average yearly mileage per car as 10,000, the last column shows the annual saving (the product of columns 3 and 4). In other words, reductions in the cost of tire mileage to the motoring public in the fifteen years, 1920–1934, have amounted to $28,166,560,000, a sum practically as large as the present national debt. This saving has resulted from the discovery and application of new and better chemicals and methods for their use.

YEAR	TIRE COST PER 10,000 MILES	1920 COST MINUS COST EACH YEAR. SAVINGS PER CAR	VEHICLE REGIS. IN MILLIONS	ANNUAL SAVINGS IN MILLIONS OF DOLLARS
1920......	$163.00	.....	.....	......
1921......	142.00	$21.00	10.46	219.72
1922......	121.00	42.00	12.24	514.00
1923......	101.00	62.00	15.09	935.70
1924......	101.00	62.00	17.60	1090.89
1925......	102.00	61.00	19.94	1216.16
1926......	89.00	74.00	22.00	1628.07
1927......	81.00	82.00	23.13	1896.91
1928......	67.00	96.00	24.49	2351.33
1929......	53.00	110.00	26.50	2915.11
1930......	44.00	119.00	26.55	3158.86
1931......	36.00	127.00	25.83	3280.79
1932......	40.00	123.00	24.12	2966.15
1933......	37.50	125.50	23.83	2990.29
1934......	38.50	124.50	24.12	3002.58

Fuel for automotive vehicles has passed through an extremely interesting history in which chemical industry and its products have been important at every step of development. To begin the story properly, one must go back to the time of a century ago when whale fisheries were the principal dependence for burning oil to supply illumination. Smelly whale-oil lamps had superseded candles for illuminating purposes and, despite the smoky, malodorous flame they gave, were the best available. The drilling of the first successful oil well by Drake in 1859 gave the world a new supply of petroleum, rock oil, among whose early uses was the lighting of homes. In early lamps, it was barely less disagreeable than the whale oil, but finally, by the application of the distillation process and subsequent refining by successive treatments with sulfuric acid and alkali, the parts causing the smell and much of the smoke were eliminated to yield a satisfactory burning oil. The development of the lamp chimney and a burner adapted to it (the Argand burner) made kerosene lamps efficient. A serious difficulty appeared as demand increased and some refiners failed to remove the gasoline and naphtha from their kerosene before it was put into lamps. Frequent explosions of lamps emphasized the need for more careful separation of these dangerous elements from burning oil and, in the course of time, loss of life and property from this cause was effectively prevented by the imposition of specifications requiring that burning oil be freed from these hazardous components. This immediately placed upon petroleum refiners the burden of finding other uses for these forced wastes at a time when the internal combustion engine was undergoing the last stages of its initial development into what later became the motive power of our automobiles. Both the engine and a ready-made fuel supply were in existence at the time that pneumatic rubber tires were first put on automobiles, and it is very probable that these were the ruling causes in the survival of the gasoline-driven car in preference to the steam car designed to use kerosene, or the electric car dependent upon frequent recharging of its storage batteries to enable it to travel within relatively restricted areas.

The demands for fuel and lubrication for automobiles soon became the most important of those supplied by the petroleum refiners and the requirements of the internal combustion engine were dominant in setting the standards of refining practice, both for fuel and for lubricants. To meet the specifications set up by automotive use, refiners continually developed improvements in their refining methods, all of which required the use of vast quantities of products of chemical manufacture. As engines were improved from a power-producing standpoint, it soon became evident that fuels must be improved to take full advantage of the best designs of the automotive engineers. One of the most significant defects of the fuels of two decades ago was the limit their tendency to detonation placed on the compression pressures possible in the engine, the increase of compression pressures being the most important method of raising the efficiency of the engine without increasing its weight. Careful investigation revealed that the addition of a number of chemical compounds, notably of tellurium, tetra-ethyl lead, benzol, and a number of others to the fuel reduced its tendency to detonate, or knock, and permitted substantial increases in the efficiency of the engine. Experience has shown that the addition of small amounts of tetra-ethyl lead together with regulated doses of ethylene

117

dibromide, both of which could be manufactured syn-thetically by the chemical industry in practically un-limited quantities, and certain compounds produced directly from the crude oil itself in the process of "cracking" described below were the most satisfactory materials available for this purpose. The effect of these distinctly chemical products has been both direct in increasing automotive efficiencies and indirect in en-couraging engine designers to improve their products. By this combined effect, it has been estimated that the automobiles of 1937 have a potential power which, if produced from fuels no better than could be made at the earlier date, would have required millions of gal-lons more of gasoline than are to be had from the whole petroleum industry.

The perfectly stupendous demand placed upon our petroleum reserves and the petroleum refining industry by the growth of the automotive industry and the spread of this method of transportation throughout the world threatened as early as 1920 to consume all the then known petroleum reserves within a very few years. This was one of the ruling motives in the development of more efficient automobile engines, but even more im-portant was the effect this had on the development of improved methods of petroleum refining and processes for making far more gasoline than had formerly been available from each barrel of crude oil sent to the re-finery. Many factors have operated to extend our use-ful oil supply in the intervening period, including the discovery of new pools, the re-forming of natural gas to yield liquid fuels, the better working of known oil fields to secure oil from wells worked out by older methods, improved drill bits using new alloys and driving even deeper, newly developed methods of acid treatment of old wells to increase their yield, the increased efficiency of use to which we have alluded above, and most important of all, the wider application of cracking processes. Yet, altogether, all of these conservational measures have merely served to postpone the day when the increased price of gasoline will force the development of new sources of fuel or new methods of utilizing known fuels. Present production of crude oil in the United States approaches a billion barrels annually.

Cracking processes are based upon the fact that the heavy molecules of the higher boiling constituents of crude petroleum can be broken into smaller molecules similar to those in gasoline by the application of heat under proper conditions. This requires that the oil in the refinery be subjected to very high temperatures while it is held under very high pressures, a condition met only by the use of modern steel alloys. By this means, it is possible to secure fifty to sixty gallons of gasoline from one hundred gallons of crude oil, which would yield by the ordinary methods of direct distillation only some twenty to twenty-five gallons of gasoline. Part of the heavy oils which go into the cracking unit is converted into gas which lends itself admirably to the uses of synthetic chemistry. The possession of sources of vast amounts of these so-called cracking gases is forming the basis of an entirely new and strictly American chemical industry. Their elaboration may be expected to become ultimately quite as important to our convenience and comfort as the elaboration of products of coal tar. Not only does the cracking of oil produce more gasoline than the previously used methods of distillation, but the gasoline it yields possesses a high anti-knock value and may be used in modern efficient engines without waste of power from knocking. Excellent gasoline of high anti-knock value is also synthesized (re-formed) from the gases from cracking. More than 180,000,000 barrels (45 per cent) of gasoline are annually produced by cracking processes.

Lubrication of early machines was accomplished by the use of various natural fats and oils from animals and particularly that from the sperm whale. The growth of industry and the increasingly varied demands made of lubricants soon reached a point where these could no longer suffice. The oiliness of petroleum and the variety of lubricants of varying properties derived from it supplied these new needs, both alone and mixed with other greases and compounds. Formerly, simple separation of oily parts of petroleum by distilllation met industry's needs, but latterly these products have been further refined and modified by chemical treatments. One of these involved the conversion of naturally occurring compounds into more useful forms by treatment with hydrogen under great pressure in the presence of a catalyst, which alters the fundamental character of the oil. Another method, lately of growing importance, consists of removing tarry constituents from the desired lubricating compounds by the use of certain solvents newly developed for the purpose. One of these, dichloro-ethyl ether, akin alike to ether and to chloroform, is made from the waste gas of the cracking of petroleum and is one of a whole host of useful solvents so made. Furfural, made from oat hulls, is also used to such a great extent in purifying lubricating oils that national advertising carries a story of the benefit of the "Furfural'd" oil film to the motorist.

The fabric of the modern automobile itself involves numerous other important contributions of chemical industry to the success of transportation. Particularly, the metals of which it is composed have been improved almost beyond recognition by the development of numerous special combinations of metals known under the general term, alloys. In their manufacture, various materials are dissolved in molten metal, just as salt or sugar might be dissolved in water, and after cooling, the whole forms a solid solution which may or may not include chemical combination between the main body of the metal and the added ingredients.

Alloy steels and alloy cast irons have long been indispensable to production of the modern automobile, rugged and reliable, and economical to purchase and maintain. Although these alloyed steels and irons have the outward appearance of the plain carbon steels that served past generations, they are virtually new materials in the possession of qualities that carbon cannot confer. To appreciate this one need only reflect that without great change in design or appearance the familiar leaf spring of the automobile has progressed from the carbon steel remembered for its faults to the alloy steel almost forgotten by reason of its virtues. Although alloy steels pervade the rear hubs and add their blessing to the front axle and steering knuckles, carbon steels hold in frame, body and fenders the place to which they are entitled by reason of excellent strength, toughness, and ease of forming. Scorning to employ alloying to compensate imperfection in carbon steels and irons, the chemistry of steelmaking has developed their inherent merits and restored their place in the sun.

Within the engine, numerous special alloys greatly increase the utility value of the various parts and make the power plant of the modern automobile a far more efficient source of motive power. Cast iron alloyed with chromium and nickel provides a cylinder block and head more easily machinable and more resistant to heat expansion and to wear, and camshafts of high-strength alloyed cast iron replace those of forged and cast steel. Passing from the massive to the minute, more than one-half of the earlier electrical trouble passed with the advent of tungsten contact points in the distributor and of nickel-barium wire at the points of the spark plug. Within less than a decade, the increase in bearing pressures required by advances in design and higher power output has forced the abandonment of the older babbitt metal bearings (made of a soft alloy of lead and tin with or without antimony) whose strength was insufficient to carry the load upon them. They have been replaced by harder and stronger bearings which range from the older copper-tin bronzes to alloys on which cadmium, calcium and even silver confer novel properties. In some of them lubrication is enhanced, although not entirely provided, by graphite dispersed in the alloy. Failures of bearings in service have become extremely rare as a consequence of this change. Valves for admitting fresh combustible mixture and for releasing exhaust gases at the proper points in the cycle of operation are subjected simultaneously to extreme conditions of high temperature and powerful pressure. These were for a period limiting factors in the design of internal combustion engines for increased power and efficiency. Silcrome, a steel alloyed with silicon and chromium, has for some years been standard for exhaust valves, and earlier troubles have almost disappeared. However, engine operation on heavy trucks is especially hard on exhaust valves and their seats, and careful owners are renewing both of these parts and prolonging their life by facing with a well-known alloy of chromium, cobalt and tungsten. Furthermore, valve seats of the alloy are frequently built into new engines intended for trucks of the better grade. The pistons of many internal combustion engines are made of the alloys of aluminum or magnesium which combine strength with extremely light weight (about one-third that of iron or steel) and thus require less power for their starting and stopping in the up and down strokes in the cylinders.

It is important to point out that the tools used in the fabrication and finishing of the metal parts of the modern automobile have had to be developed progressively as each step in improving the ultimate product

123

has been taken. Tools made of alloys of steel or other metals, perfected to permit a rate of machining many times greater than any possible with the older carbon steel tools, and improved oils for lubricating and cooling tools have been fundamental to the quantity manufacture of automobiles at prices within reach of the vast number of their present owners. All of the high-speed tools hold full hardness at the cutting edge when run so fast as to remain red hot. Those used in the machining of steel are forged steels highly alloyed with chromium, tungsten and vanadium, to which cobalt is often added. For the cutting of steel or cast iron, tools cast from an alloy of chromium, tungsten and cobalt are standard in many large shops, while highest speeds in the machining of cast iron are reached with the hardest of cutting tools, in which tungsten carbide bound with cobalt are the best known. To build any of the low-priced models in 1937 by the machine-shop methods of twenty years ago would so lengthen the fabrication operation that not more than some 10 per cent of the output required could be manufactured, and the price that would have to be demanded for the few that could be built would be several hundred per cent higher than those now prevailing. No less marvellous is the precision with which electric smelting furnaces produce from raw ores ferroalloys and alloying metals that year after year meet close and exacting specifications of analysis and purity, and the certainty with which the electric steel furnace pours hundreds of heats standard not only in chemical composition but also in physical properties of the alloyed steels thus produced. Not only are the cutting tools of the machine shop far more efficient today than ever before, but many parts previously assembled at great labor are now quickly stamped in gigantic stamping machines from sheets through improvements in stamping tools.

The marvellous ways in which the properties of metals can be modified by the addition of proper alloying elements is among the great achievements of modern times. The purification of the many ingredients of modern alloys and their preparation for use has reached huge proportions as part of the chemical industry and has put into practice a technic of its own. Since high temperatures are uniformly involved, electric furnaces capable of producing heat at previously unimaginable high levels have been perfected, and in them a multitude of useful products is made, varying through the numerous useful metals and their alloys to artificial abrasives approaching the diamond in hardness; graphite, so soft as to be a valuable lubricant; and calcium carbide, which supplies us with acetylene for the preparation of numerous important synthetic products, including the most successful synthetic rubber-like material yet made.

Four other important products used in the modern motor car are direct products of chemical industry: particularly the safety glass now required by law in most states; upholstery, originally of leather but now almost entirely of artificial leather; moulded parts made from synthetic resins or other plastics for insulation purposes or because they can be made better in this way than from metals; and finally the lacquer coating which is applied instead of varnish with the saving of time of actual weeks per car.

Safety glass, made by cementing two pieces of glass to a non-brittle sheet of synthetic transparent material, has saved countless lives and a vast amount of human suffering from the cuts which so magnified the damage from accidents in cars equipped with ordinary plate glass. Both the glass itself and the safety layer cemented between are direct products of chemical industry.

The leather upholstery of the earlier automobiles is rapidly giving way before the use of fabric finishes in modern closed cars, yet even the reduced demand for a leather-like finish would be impossible to supply from the hides of animals without literally over-running the country with cattle. Imitation leather made by applying a surface of nitrocellulose or rubber to fabrics and even reinforced paper had long replaced leather made from hides before the vogue for closed cars reduced the importance of this type of finish. In modern closed cars, the use of a similar prepared fabric still survives as the roof covering, and for this use alone many millions of square yards are consumed annually.

The stories of synthetic resins and the fabrication from them of countless small objects of value and beauty and of the modern nitrocellulose lacquers, so important in the automobile industry, can be more properly told in connection with electrical communication and with the protective coatings applied to our homes and their contents. The reader is referred to the chapters dealing with these subjects.

Successful operation of internal combustion engines in both automobiles and airplanes requires that the cylinders be kept cool, ordinarily by the circulation of water cooled in a radiator provided for the purpose. In cold weather there is danger of freezing of this water to the serious damage of the engine, and consequently chemical industry has been called upon to supply materials to be added to the cooling water to lower its freezing point to such a degree that danger from this cause is eliminated. Many things have been used, but the most widely accepted today are denatured alcohol, made from grain, molasses or by synthesis; glycerine, product of the soap industry, and the basic material for the manufacture of nitroglycerol; synthetic methanol, long familiar as wood alcohol; ethylene glycol, and a number of other synthetic alcohols made from the waste gases of petroleum refining. The value of antifreeze materials consumed by the automobile drivers in the United States is insignificant in comparison with the other costs of driving, and their cheapness and wide distribution have changed the driving habits of the nation since it is no longer necessary to do without the comforts and conveniences of automotive travel for fear of cold.

The electric storage battery upon which the successful operation of the engine depends is essentially a series of chemically produced lead plates hardened and stiffened with antimony, coated with oxides of lead and suspended in a solution of chemically pure sulfuric acid contained in a chemically produced resinous box. The contributions of chemical industry to this vitalizing power accessory are obvious from their mere enumeration. The next improvement in storage batteries may be expected from the replacement of antimony by calcium, already shown to be better.

On the subject of electric batteries, it is necessary to note the efficacy of modern dry cells as convenient portable sources of electricity for performing innumerable valuable tasks. These batteries whose efficiency has been steadily raised through research are strictly products of chemical industry from the graphitized carbon in its chemically produced medium housed in a chemically pure zinc case to the resin which seals it shut. Storage batteries for special purposes are made also with nickel and nickel alloys in an alkaline liquid to function as reservoirs of electric power.

The rapid and successful development of liquid fuels as the source of power in internal combustion engines, upon which the automobile depends, has had a significant effect in giving us our present means of transportation through the air. If the evolution be traced to its ultimate beginnings, one may very properly say that the placing of a rubber tire on a wheel led through the automobile age to the era of aviation. The steps of that development were: the rubber-tired wheel of the bicycle, made more comfortable by being inflated with air in the "safeties" of the gay nineties, put under the horseless carriages of the next decade to convert them into automobiles, which required the self-contained power plants ideally adapted to furnish the power for the flight of man. Thus, one may say that the development of satisfactory rubber for the construction of pneumatic tires has given us the two most important modern means of swift transportation over land and in the air.

In the adaptation of automobile engines to flight, the ruling factor has been the increase in efficiency of power production with a simultaneous reduction in weight, a consideration of the utmost importance in heavier-than-air flying where increased weight requires increased power to keep it aloft. The lightweight alloys of aluminum and magnesium and the alloy steels, possessing strength per unit of weight far greater than that of unalloyed steels, have been of essential service in the development of all-metal airplanes or replace their less safe and dependable predecessors whose wings were of fabric stretched by the application of nitro-cellulose lacquers. Airplane travel has been rendered far safer through use of alloy metals and alloy steels in various parts of the construction. On the engine, exhaust valves and their seats are now usually provided with inserts of a heat- and corrosion-resistant alloy of chromium, cobalt and tungsten, and the excess heat is conducted from the valves by a core of metallic sodium extending through the valve stem. To combat oxidation in other quarters even the exhaust pipe is welded from heat-resistant high chromium sheet steel, and sea-water corrosion is resisted by pontoons of chromium-nickel steel sheet stabilized with alloyed columbium. Chromium-molybdenum steel tubing jointed by oxy-acetylene welding is now standard, and failure of such framing has not yet been recorded. For every part of the construction the materials are selected, tested, fabricated and assembled with the utmost care and precision of which engineering science is capable. Fuel economy as a load-reducing measure has been more important in aviation than it has been in automobiles, where its only importance to date has been in making travel more economical. The modern airplane may be truthfully said to be a combination of products of the chemical industry, fabricated according to the designs of skillful engineers, which, in many respects, have been based on automobiles and soaring birds.

The ancient art of navigation and the trade of the men who go down to the sea in ships has not been without its debt to chemical industry. In addition to many materials adopted by shipping from other fields, it is supplied with special paints in wide variety to meet the severe conditions of marine service. The anti-fouling paints, which have universally replaced the sheet copper nailed to the bottoms of wooden ships from time immemorial, are of special composition embodying both the protection of a paint and the poisonous character of the germicides of medicine and the insecticides and fungicides of agriculture. The problem differs from any other type of painting in that the coating must be relatively permanent for a long period of time, yet it must slowly disintegrate to release poisons which will kill marine growths and borers before they have an opportunity to attach themselves to the vessel. This problem has been successfully solved in a number of different ways that meet the conditions imposed both by the yachtsman intent on speed and sport, and his more serious confrères who carry freight and passengers upon the deep or harvest the manifold crops of the sea.

The corrosion of iron and steel of the hulls or other parts of ships is much more serious than in other uses of these metals, yet their relative cheapness has thus far deterred extensive replacement by metals or alloys more resistant to corrosion; but beginnings have been made. On some yachts the standing rigging and all of the metal trim, both deck and interior, are provided in chromium-nickel stainless steel. On submarines some of the deck equipment is already built, and on large naval craft parts of the superstructure are specified to be constructed of chromium-nickel steel. In the merchant marine this steel has taken a deserved place in the lighter superstructure of the *Normandie* and the *Queen Mary,* the newest of our great passenger liners. In the past decades sea-water corrosion has been counteracted by application of protective paint coatings to keep away from metal parts of ships the salt water of the sea and the spray which blows from it. The severity of this service has been met by the development of special paints which are as nearly as can be completely waterproof. Spar varnishes for marine use are also specially made from ingredients, including synthetic resins, produced by chemical industry. The protection of marine pilings from borers and fish nets from destruction and decay have utilized, among other things, the weapons developed for fighting chemical wars.

Fireworks, ordinarily considered to be the din-producing fire crackers of Fourth of July celebrations, perform essential services in the safety of transportation by land, by sea and by air. Signal flares warning of danger, rockets calling help at sea, and illuminating flares to assist the aviator in finding his landing save uncounted lives of travellers. The branch of chemical industry engaged in the manufacture of these essentials produces other explosives having value elsewhere. Despite its importance, the pyrotechnic industry is not even honored in census reports by being accorded a separate listing. Yet, without its products the danger of storm and the hazards of travel would be enormously magnified.

With the general adoption of the wheel in transportation in the far-flung territory of America, chemical industry in its then crude form may be said to have begun its contribution to the movement of man and his goods from place to place. Both the vehicles and the roads over which they travelled, in fact all forms of transportation have undergone continuous improvement through the accumulated genius of invention and the increased contribution of chemical manufacture to the materials available for inventive use.

6.

From Papyrus to Television

OF ALL those things which distinguish modern civilization from that of our forefathers, none is so striking as the development of means of communication of intelligence over vast distances of time and space. One must distinguish between rapidity of communication, whose objective is to convey intelligence over long distances, and permanence of communication, whose records bridge intervals of time. The latter has its origins in the most distant antiquity and hence is entitled to first consideration here even though it lack the spectacular quality inherent in Morse's experiments of a century ago with the electric telegraph.

133

The art of recording thought, invented ages ago, initiated history and differentiates prehistoric men from their successors who were able to accumulate experience from generation to generation. Despite its vital importance to the subsequent advance of civilization, the writing and recording of facts were dependent on the materials available. Not until man began to master the materials Nature provided and to adapt and alter them to his purposes did this art assume its essential role in human affairs. The cumbersome carving of stones, fashioning clay into tiles, the papyrus of the Egyptians and the Romans, the medieval production of manuscripts on parchmentized skins of animals, and the crudities of the earliest methods of printing all show the extraordinary progress since made on the basis of better materials for writing and printing.

Properly, the subject of writing and printing divides itself into two material phases: paper and ink. To both of these chemical industry, through its manifold services in the preparation of materials, has substantially contributed.

The vast and obvious difference between a standing forest or bales of old rags and the numerous varieties of paper with which we come in daily contact is a chemical change from raw material to another form more serviceable to man brought about by the use of products of chemical manufacture. The simplest papers are made by the mere mechanical disintegration of fibrous materials—wood, flax or other plant stems —into individual fibers followed by matting these together. The resulting sheets are weak, easily destroyed by the action of air or relatively minor mechanical wear and so absorbent of ink as to be of very limited value. Paper of a sort can be made by that simple process, but to make it really useful other materials must be incorporated: a bleach to whiten the product, a size to improve the bond between the fibers and increase the strength of the sheet, and filler to reduce its absorptive capacity for ink. To produce a satisfactory material, more complicated operations must be undertaken to separate the pure cellulose from undesired parts of the plant. These methods, of which three are practiced on huge scales and several others to a minor extent, are based upon the use of chemical products so chosen that they dissolve away everything but the cellulose itself and leave that in condition for use. The first product of such an operation is a relatively pure cellulose in the form known as pulp, which upon further appropriate additions and treatments yields commercial paper. The ultimate purpose the paper is to serve determines the kind and extent of these processes.

All methods of pulping cellulose materials require the use of products of chemical industry. The most important method is the so-called sulfite process in which wood chips are boiled under pressure with a solution of calcium and magnesium acid sulfites (made by running water in which sulfur dioxide is dissolved over limestone or dolomite). This treatment frees the cellulose from extraneous matter and puts it, after washing and bleaching, in a form to be felted into sheets ready to be made into paper. The soda process and the sulfate process are similar, except that they employ alkaline cooking liquors, which permit the use of woods of high rosin content such as the pines. Up to the present time, the sulfate pulps were used largely in the manufacture of coarse papers such as wrapping, but with the recent improvements in bleaching methods, bleached sulfate pulps are produced of sufficient whiteness to be used in high grade papers. Soda pulps are usually bleached and used in many high grade papers requiring softness and bulk.

In the manufacture of paper from pulp, numerous other chemical products are required. Already bleaching, which utilizes chlorine, has been mentioned. Even this does not completely whiten paper and small amounts of color are added to counteract the residual yellow tint that is not removed by the bleaching operation and thus give white papers a more pleasing appearance. The felting of the individual fibers into a coherent sheet requires the use of a bonding agent, often a soap made from and containing rosin which also prevents too rapid absorption of ink. Many other proofing and surfacing materials may also be incorporated. The highest quality printing papers are given a smooth glossy surface to receive the impressions of fine engravings by coating with casein (made from milk) and white pigments.

In the manufacture of various fancy papers to secure particular effects, other products of chemical industry largely enter. Not only are decorative effects secured through the use of dyes, metal powders, and other things introduced during the felting process, but other effects are produced by pressing or embossing with raised or engraved rolls on the paper as a finishing operation. Special papers for purposes other than printing and writing are made by other chemical processes. Treatment with sulfuric acid yields a parchment-like sheet. Glazing and waterproofing compounds including paraffin wax make the finished sheet more resistant to wetting and increase its transparency. The addition of certain drying oils makes transparent windows in envelopes.

The preparation of the new transparent cellulose sheet materials is not stirctly related to the manufacture of paper, being in reality a branch of the rayon industry which will be considered later, but the product is in some respects so closely competitive with paper that it must be mentioned here. In essence, the process consists in dissolving cellulose to form a solution of honey-like consistency and precipitating the cellulose from this solution after it has been squirted through a thin opening. The result is a transparent, glistening sheet which can be made pliable by the addition of suitable materials such, for instance, as glycerine and may be rendered moisture resistant by applying suitable coatings. A more detailed description of its manufacture and its economic effects will be found in a later chapter.

This discussion of paper would be incomplete without mention of the special finishes used on that intended for important documents, bank checks, stock certificates and the like, to prevent fradulent changes in written or printed words. The method involved consists essentially in applying a coating to the surface of the paper (or within its fabric during manufacture) which gives an immediate warning by change of color or otherwise of any attempted alteration. The materials used for this purpose may be extremely fugitive dyes or other compounds which fade or change color when attempts at erasure are made. Similarly, special papers consisting of combinations of colored and uncolored fibers are used for making counterfeiting difficult and easily detectable, as in United States paper currency.

Inks are essentially products of chemical industry. Four general classes of inks are recognized according to the purpose for which they are intended and the method of their use. Writing, engraving, printing, and lithographing inks in general vary in consistency in the order named, from the thin watery ink used in pens through thicker, oily engraving and printing inks to semi-solid lithographic inks. Writing inks are solutions of coloring matter in water, the simplest being made of tannic acid (extracted from nutgalls or barks of trees) and a soluble compound or iron (copperas, iron sulfate) dissolved in water to which certain gums have been added to give the right consistency. Other writing inks contain water-soluble dyes of appropriate colors and simply dye the parts of the paper with which they come into contact.

Printing inks, on the other hand, are made by grinding together an oil and an insoluble pigment. For black ink, linseed oil or a varnish made from it and mineral oil is commonly the vehicle and various carbon blacks made from oil flames, gas flames or carbonized bones constitute the pigment. The desired consistency is secured by employing a thick viscous oil and when necessary adding a solvent to thin the mixture, the solvent evaporating from the printed work and leaving the ink behind. Colored printing inks are made with appropriate pigments, either natural or synthetic. Ordinarily, the natural pigments do not possess the desired brilliancy of color and consequently most colored inks are made with pigments especially prepared for the purpose from synthetic dyestuffs or by chemical precipitation of mineral compounds.

It is apparent from these facts that the art of printing draws its supplies from sources also used in other industries. Its paper is manufactured from the same trees and by the same processes which yield the raw material for the rayon industry which supplies clothing, for the lacquer industry whose product is a decorative and protective coating and for the nitrocellulose of smokeless powder. Its inks are in most respects similar to oil paints, and the oils and varnishes used in them are practically the same as those which the paint maker uses. The pigments which give color to printing inks are made from dyestuffs in all respects similar to those which color our clothing and which are closely related to our beneficent synthetic medicines.

The value of printed products exceeds 1.9 billion dollars per annum, a substantial industry built upon the consumption of relatively small amounts of chemical products.

It would be improper to pass over the art of printing

without briefly describing the services chemical industry renders in the reproduction of illustrations through the processes of photoengraving and electrotyping. Elsewhere, the methods of photography and the recording of pictures will be discussed. Photoengraving depends, like photography, on changes in the properties of certain materials when exposed to light. In photography, the change is produced in a film containing silver salts. Photoengraving depends upon the alteration produced by light in a gelatin film containing chromium compounds. This change is of such a nature that the affected portions of a film on a metal plate can be made to resist the action of etching solutions on the metal and yield a relief after the unprotected parts are eaten away by the acid. Appropriate differences in treatment produce the different kinds of plates needed for printing and lithographing processes and for applying the various colors of colored prints separately. The advantages of these processes over the older arts are evident from a comparison of any specimen of modern printing with one of a hundred years ago before photochemical methods of reproduction were devised.

The photoengraving industry consumes great quantities of many products of chemical industry in providing us with permanent records of events and scenes all over the world, from the transient tabloid newspaper to such superb reproductions of photographs as regularly appear in the *National Geographic Magazine* and other artistically designed publications.

The processes of photography are all very strictly

based upon products of chemical industry of which the photographic industry forms an important part. The wide use of photography has contributed so essentially to human progress, enjoyment and happiness, that some of its applications must be mentioned here. The fundamental process of recording images by photography depends upon the changes produced in certain compounds of silver by light. Some other substances, notably certain of the synthetic dyes, increase this sensitivity to light which permits their use in certain special variations of photography. Recent advances in the art of photography utilize the invisible infra-red rays in such a way that pictures can actually be made of objects that cannot be seen. This is particularly important in navigation and aviation through murk and mist, since the infra-red rays easily penetrate through and allow objects to be "seen" by the infra-red camera which are invisible to the unaided eye. This development has been applied to making photographs through the human skin and in another field enables burned documents to be read.

The ability of photographic films to see and record the invisible has entirely changed both astronomy and microscopy, with the very important result that the eyes of the observer are now far less important than his films. Photomicrography, as applied in the field of medicine, has resulted in the saving of innumerable lives. Photographic films are also extremely sensitive to the invisible ultraviolet rays and allow pictures to be made of objects in radiation of this kind that would otherwise be invisible to the human eye. Not only are the frontiers of knowledge being pushed farther into the unknown in the fields of the infinitely great (astronomy) and of the infinitely small (microscopy) but the processes of mapping areas (geography) have been improved by photography with the elimination of much human drudgery and important savings of time.

The ramifications of photography take one easily into the realm of art. The latest remarkable development of colored photographs provides pictures, both still and in motion, in all the natural colors of the original subject with far greater fidelity than any artist could achieve. This, like so many other modern wonders, has been built upon the gradual accomplishment of numerous lesser objectives upon which the final achievement is based. Special types of developers and dyes sensitive both to them and to light, as well as new types of emulsions, were necessary before the perfection of present-day color photographs on a single film could be accomplished. In the drama and in music, the faithful recording of sound photographically, as exemplified in our talking pictures of today, is no less important a contribution of chemical industry than the sound recording discs and cylinders of talking machines. The essential differences are that sounds were mechanically recorded on a chemically produced resin and now they are put on a chemically produced film by means of a varying beam of light.

Incidental to the vast improvement of photography in recent years has been a constant requirement for new and rare chemical compounds for experimental as well as practical use in connection with its processes.

This particular demand encouraged a leading photographic manufacturer, George Eastman, during the World War, to put at the disposal of the chemical industry, without profit, the products of his small-scale manufacture. With thousands of rare and unusual products thus available to research workers in many apparently remote fields, the important tasks of finding new and better ways to do things have been facilitated beyond calculation and the whole people of the United States are deep in his debt.

The earliest means of communication at a distance, as distinct from the bridging of time with recorded thought, was by couriers running in relays from place to place. The ancient kings of the Medes and the Persians set up intricate systems of courier relays by which the vast dominions of their empire could communicate with one another within a matter of days. Signal fires, drums, and smokes were also important early means of hurriedly covering distance. The heliograph, in which a small mirror reflects the sun's light to a remote point and by flashes and pauses transmits messages, was presumably developed by the ancient Mayans in Mexico. The origin of the semaphore is lost in antiquity. None of these methods of transmitting messages at a distance was wholly dependable or always effective, but until the early nineteenth century, they were the best available.

The great step forward in the art of rapid communication dates from the experiments of Samuel F. B. Morse in 1835 with his crude devices from which the electric telegraph grew. At this early date, the only source of useful electric energy to operate his instruments was the chemical reaction occurring in a crude electric battery. Even today, electricity from chemical batteries (gravity cells using copper, zinc and copper sulfate or the more modern dry cells) is used to a large extent in telegraph service and for many decades these were the sole sources of the vitalizing current of our telegraph systems. Along with the spread of our great network of railroads, the telegraph proved itself so valuable that it, too, penetrated throughout the country and supplied nation-wide communication that chopped days, and even weeks, from the time required to send a message from one point to another over this continent. The most important requirement of the telegraph, in addition to the batteries originally used to supply its power, was wire of very low electrical resistance. Ordinary copper wire was not good enough. Its inefficiency was due largely to impurities present in minute amounts that could not be removed by the older refining methods. This demand ultimately supplied impetus to the perfection of the electrolytic method of refining copper by which all objectionable impurities tending to lower the conductivity of the wire are brought to an irreducible minimum. This method, as now practised by the chemical industry, places copper for electrical purposes among the purest commercial materials.

The land telegraph proved so valuable that it was ultimately adapted to use under seas to set up communication between continents. This introduced new complications because of the extreme length of the lines, the necessity for protecting and insulating them from the sea, and the relatively large amounts of electric power needed to overcome the resistance of such long circuits. In solving all of these problems, chemical industry played an important part, supplying a purer copper to reduce resistance, a variety of water-resistant materials to provide insulation, and more powerful batteries to provide the needed current. One of the most recent contributions of chemistry to the efficiency of submarine cables has been the perfection of a nickel-iron alloy (permalloy) which, when built into the sheathing of the cable, materially reduces the loss of current from induction between the wire and the surrounding sea water.

To the next improvement in electrical communication, chemical industry has contributed even more essentially. Bell's telephone depended for its operation on a microphone capable of transforming sound waves into a pulsating electric current which would regenerate similar sound waves when converted into magnetic impulses acting on a flexible steel diaphragm in the receiver. This microphone as developed consisted of small pieces of carbon whose contact with each other (and hence the electric resistance between them) varied as the impulses of sound waves are imparted to them by the transmitter diaphragm. These little carbon grains are still vital to the success of the telephone as a means of communication, and upon their manufacture has been expended a vast amount of research by both the electrical industry, which uses them, and the chemical industry, which supplies them. Without the improvements resulting from this cooperation and research, the modern long-distance telephone communication which we take so much for granted would be quite impossible. The quantity of these carbon granules consumed annually is triflingly small, but upon their successful conversion of sound waves into electrical impulses, the success of our entire telephone system depends.

Numerous other parts essential to the smooth operation of our modern telephone system have been supplied by chemical industry. The storage batteries into which chemical or mechanical rectifiers of alternating current pour the energy required to activate the system; the insulation which keeps circuits apart in the vast networks of chemically purified copper wires; the special alloys required for contact points, magnetic cores for transformers and coils and other essential parts of the system; telephone instruments themselves and their finishes, largely synthetic products of chemical manufacture; the immense amounts of rubber required in all parts of the system; the relay tubes adapted and adopted from the infant radio industry; these are but a few of the many essentials to telephonic communication which are products of chemical industry. Even the removal of moisture from the air of cable terminals and exchanges in climates where high humidity interferes with perfect performance is accomplished by the use of chemical driers.

Marconi's invention of wireless communication, and the initiation of safety on the sea through its use, was a precursor to the work of Fleming, De Forest and Langmuir on the development of the electronic relay

tube upon which rests modern voice and sound transmission without wires. It is not germane to this discussion to detail the early methods of wireless which utilized the Hertzian waves of the ether for communication between remote points beyond the statement that these early discoveries provided the foundation on which subsequent developments have erected the imposing structures of the radio and the transcontinental and transoceanic telephone. In studies of the incandescant light bulb, some extremely interesting and important conclusions were reached regarding the gradual disintegration of a filament heated to the temperature required to give light. It was found that the intensely hot filament could give off negative electrons which could be collected by a positively charged plate brought within the bulb. By constructing special tubes having plates of this kind, a sensitive instrument was produced for detecting the electromagnetic energy received by a wireless antenna from the ether. This was the two-element tube so called because it consisted of a hot filament and a target or plate. Later it was made far more useful by placing between these elements a grid to which are transmitted the tiny charges generated externally by radio waves. In this way, the number of charged particles from the filament reaching the plate, and hence the flow of current, could be much more exactly controlled.

After this development was made, the problem became one of increasing the rate of flow of electrons, as these infinitesimal charged particles are called, by making the filament from which they are generated of a

material yielding them more readily and by creating
within the containing glass tube a much more complete
vacuum which would offer the least possible hindrance
to their passage. Several elements offered themselves
as solving the first part of the problem since they have
the ability to shoot off electrons even at relatively low
temperatures. Thorium, cerium, cesium, barium, and
strontium in the form of their compounds were supplied by chemical industry for this purpose and the
capacity of the early electron valves was vastly increased. It was shown to be unnecessary to heat these
new filaments to the very high temperatures of glowing
to produce the desired result and now it is common
practice to heat a surface containing these elements
indirectly by a tiny coil of very fine wire so that alternating current may be utilized to energize the electron
generators of vacuum tubes. Thus the operation of the
family radio set was made independent of the use of
batteries requiring frequent renewals.

The increased ease of flow of the electron stream
was accomplished by greatly increasing the vacuum in
the tube by using what are technically known as "getters" to remove the last traces of air which cannot be
drawn out by any amount of pumping. "Getters" are
chemical compounds which combine with these residual
traces of gases to form solid materials and thereby remove gaseous molecules from the electron path. Magnesium, barium, strontium and combinations of them
combine with both oxygen and nitrogen and are the
getters most often employed. Coatings of these metals
produced in the process impart the bright mirror to

the inner surface of the glass wall of the vacuum tube.

Only tiny amounts of these several products of chemical industry are required in the manufacture of a single vacuum tube (an ounce of them will serve for literally thousands of tubes). Their vital importance to the successful operation of modern radio and the enormous numbers of such tubes made (running into the millions annually) have created new demands for hitherto very rare materials, so rare in fact that their principal former value was in decorating sundry museum cases. This, of course, is not strictly true, for gas lighting, which passed with the perfection of modern electric lighting methods, used some of these same types of electron-emitting elements in its gas mantles which gave greater luminosity to the pale flame of gas. It is true that this use of rare elements possessing electron emitting power did not recognize this important property, but the technic of supplying and purifying them was developed ready to hand when their value for radio was at last recognized.

Vital as are these contributions of chemical industry to modern radio, they do not by any means exhaust the list of its important services to the new art. The impulses received by the radio set are almost unimaginably small and the thing necessary to make them audible and intelligible is not only to detect them but also to use their most minute variations. The problems encountered in passing them through a system which will magnify them many millionfold without distortion thus become evident. Mechanical precision of the highest type must be employed in constructing the numerous parts of the apparatus and the selection of material must be made with the utmost care to avoid even the slightest and apparently most insignificant leakages of current or distortion of its variations. The prodigious magnification of any faults in the system is greater than any other magnification employed anywhere else in any human activity. An impulse so small as to be almost undetectable with even the finest and most delicate instruments is used to control current great enough to operate, in the extreme case, sound volumes audible for several miles.

The first care in handling such minute currents is to insulate them so completely from leakages that none of the tiny impulse is lost and that no stray current from casual sources is introduced into the circuit. Glass and porcelain insulators adopted from other electrical applications serve well in some parts of the circuit, but their mechanical properties do not suit them for other equally important parts where the requirement is easy fabrication, extremely high electrical resistance and permanent retention of shape and size. Hard rubber made by introducing relatively large amounts of sulfur into rubber before vulcanization possesses these qualities to a high degree but for the fabrication of precision parts requiring permanently exact dimensions its tendency to deformation, what is termed "cold flow," rules it out. In its stead new materials, definitely products of American chemical ingenuity and American chemical industry, have been synthesized which are ideally adapted to numerous important applications in radio. So valuable are these materials, not only in this and other electrical fields where their insulation value is of importance, but in a wide diversity of other human activities, that it will be well at this point to devote some considerable attention to the synthetic resins.

To begin at the beginning and bring together the many important threads of discovery and ingenuity which have formed the basis of this distinctly American industry, we must recall the imperfections of the natural resins—widely used in certain industries—and the attempts made to improve germicides in the early days of antisepsis. Natural resins are the exudates of trees, of which the most familiar are common rosin from the gum of pine trees and shellac exuded by certain oriental insects. They possess a certain solubility in various solvents and can thus be spread over a wide area in the form of a thin coating left after the solvent has evaporated. When melted they can be molded more or less successfully and they are in general non-conductors of electricity.

The natural resins, like many other products of Nature, are likely to be variable materials containing more or less trash of various kinds and having a wide range of properties depending on their source and methods of collection. Efforts to standardize them have been generally futile as Nature has always resisted man's efforts to force her to standardize her products exactly to meet his requirements. An American chemist, Leo H. Baekeland, already famous for his invention of Velox photographic paper, became interested early in the present century in the problem of making a synthetic shellac which would be always uniform and lacking in the faults of the natural gum. As his starting point, he used the discarded results of a German chemist who, years before, had attempted to secure a super-shellac by combining carbolic acid and formalin but who had given up in disgust when all he got for his pains was a sticky disagreeable mess which he could not even crystallize. The failure of these efforts to produce germ killers gave Baekeland exactly the kind of starting material he sought, for the most obvious property of resins is their inability to form definite crystals. With this as a starting point, Baekeland bent his efforts to control the reaction between phenol and formaldehyde so that he could predict in advance just what the result of his combinations would be like. He desired a resin which would dissolve in alcohol and which would soften and flow easily in a mold, as shellac does. Instead, his products of countless experiments, while refusing to crystallize and hence resinous in character, also refused to dissolve in the many solvents he tried and instead of softening when heated, actually became harder and harder. Here was a kettle of fish. Try as he might, no other result could he obtain. Every time he heated his mixture to the point where it lost its stickiness, it became hard and insoluble. In this quandary of disappointment, instead of striving further toward an unattainable goal or giving up in disgust, Baekeland had the forethought to realize that his new substance, anomalous though its properties were, might be very useful in other ways and set about to learn how to utilize its peculiar qualities. The result was our first synthetic resin. So valuable has it become in widely divergent ways that it has been followed by whole hosts of other synthetic resins possessing other valuable properties.

Bakelite, the trade name by which the new product was called, possessed great electrical insulating value and the ability to bind other materials together permanently in a very desirable way, particularly since it did not soften when warmed. Its earliest applications were in the electrical industry in the insulation of the coils of wire used in dynamos and motors where its ability to hold them permanently in place was only less important than its protective insulating value. It was early found useful in molding small parts hitherto laboriously fashioned from other materials and particularly was it valuable in the construction of noiseless gears, in which it functioned as a binding material in a fibrous mass imparting both strength and wear resistance. Later, the development of radio required what are known as resonant electric circuits consisting of combinations of coils and condensers, and Bakelite was found very useful indeed in the making of the precise parts needed to minimize the inherent electrical losses and to insure extreme accuracy of dimension.

Chemists have since found that numerous other combinations of materials similarly produce resins and now an almost infinite variety of synthetic resins having the widest range of properties to fit them to a multitude of applications is on the market. Resins that can be dyed in almost any color, transparent resins, opaque resins, hard resins, soft resins, soluble resins, insoluble resins; indeed the list of even the variations of properties becomes ponderous. All of these, made by the ounce or by the ton as occasion requires, are produced by the chemical industry utilizing raw materials of an almost equally wide variety.

We have already suggested some of the contributions of chemical industry to the high vacuum tubes which constitute the sensitive brain of modern radio, but we have not mentioned the essential service performed in the perfection of special glasses for their construction which permits them to be fabricated by the millions on automatic machines. The technic of this art was largely developed in the manufacture of incandescent electric light bulbs, but in its application to the much more complicated assembly of the several essential elements of a radio tube, further development of both the chemical and physical qualities of glass itself was necessary. This phase of glass manufacture closely relates to the significant economies effected in the field of electric lighting, of radio as a means of communication and amusement and of the modern powerful X-ray equipment useful in industry and in diagnostic and curative medicine. These uses of glass are typical of the manifold value to be obtained from a single major development in a number of different fields through the functions of chemical industry.

In connection with telephonic communication, we have noted the importance of the tiny carbon granules in the transmitter microphone by which sound waves are converted into electrical impulses. In radio, the faithfulness of this conversion was not sufficiently accurate for the full artistic development of its possibilities and other types of microphones were perfected. One of these involves the use of specially made condensers so arranged as to be susceptible to the vibrations of sound waves. Necessarily, these condensers must function accurately and with an absolute minimum of electrical leakage which would make itself evident in extraneous noise. This, too, required special materials of construction and insulation furnished by chemical industry. Another type of microphone is based on the effect of slight variations of pressure caused by sound waves on certain pure crystals, notably Rochelle salt, and yields extremely accurate sound reproduction in the electrical circuit. These improved microphones have made radio broadcasting a vehicle for art instead of a mere mechanical marvel.

Metals have, of course, played parts of primary importance in radio development. After sound has been transformed into electrical impulses, these must be magnified before their conversion into ether waves, and after the ether waves have been caught and again transformed into electrical impulses, these must be magnified to make them strong enough to cause receivers to yield audible sound. In this process of magnification of electrical impulses, transformers similar in most respects to those used in high power transmission on lines are required. Early it was found that the ordinary steels used in power transformers were not good enough to insure distortionless amplification of the impulses in radio circuits. Consequently, efforts were made to determine what kinds of steels and what annealing and tempering conditions gave the best results. In the chapter on transportation has been noted the importance of the ferro alloys in many fields. Here again they proved of the greatest importance for it was found that steel containing relatively large proportions of silicon, heat treated in particular ways, avoided the inaccuracies of reproduction inherent in the older non-silicon steel transformers and thus improved the quality of radio transmission and reception.

An interesting example of the electrical use of chemical products is the photoelectric cell now much used in industry which is destined to make possible the development of machinery to perform operations now requiring the use of the human eye. These photoelectric cells have an electrode of silver (or copper) which is oxidized by an electric discharge in oxygen. Then metallic cesium is introduced which partly reduces the silver oxide. The final device depends upon the single layer of cesium atoms on top of a layer containing silver and silver oxide.

The element, selenium, has the valuable property of light-sensitivity. When selenium is exposed to light, its electrical resistance drops sharply, a characteristic used in cells for detecting and measuring light.

Another interesting application of chemistry in the radio field is that modern tubes are being constructed with metal envelopes. These have been made possible by the development of an alloy of nickel, iron and cobalt which has the same coefficient of expansion as glass from room temperature right up to the point at which the glass softens.

Television, which will enable future generations to see, as well as hear, at a distance, is being built upon the foundation of radio and modern optics with the aid of the essentially chemical photoelectric cell. Its beginnings are as yet too young for one to be able surely to forecast its course, but it is safe to say that whatever its ultimate form will be, it, too, will depend closely on chemical industry's products.

It is apparent, therefore, that the development of the radio industry, now valued at hundreds of millions of dollars, from the crude beginnings of wireless telegraphy three decades ago to the widespread dissemination to the whole people of the highest forms of drama and music, has been largely based on the supply of new materials by chemical industry.

7.

All the Comforts of Home

IF WE examine those needs of everyday life which are essential parts of modern civilization, chemical industry will everywhere be found contributing largely and importantly to our welfare. Clothing and housing clearly illustrate the differences between our present age and that of our forebears. These methods of protecting ourselves from the elements depend intimately on the services of science as applied in industry.

CLOTHING

Textile manufacture, one of America's great industries, rests securely upon the foundation of supplies elaborated for its use in America's chemical factories. Wool, silk, cotton and linen, the natural fibers which form the basic materials of our clothing, must undergo numerous treatments to fit them for the purpose of the spinner and weaver before they become fabrics satisfactory to be made into our clothing. Not only are the operations of creating value in the crude fibers of Nature large consumers of chemical products, but within the past two decades chemical ingenuity has created a whole new set of valuable man-made fibers—the rayons. These synthetic fibers, produced from raw materials otherwise unsuited for textile fabrication in a form more exactly suited to man's purposes, are definitely chemical manufactures.

Numerous essential differences between the modern methods of textile industry and those practiced in the primitive fireside spinning and weaving of less than a century ago are apparent. The application of machines to the problems of spinning, knitting and weaving has not only relieved men and women of drudgery but in a very important way has opened opportunities for the development of a whole train of improvements in the manufacture of clothing. The processing of fibers on the large scale required by the swifter output of power spindles and looms has forced the development of equally rapid methods of supplying them with raw material and subsequent treating of finished fabric.

It is not germane to this discussion to describe the effects of such purely mechanical improvements as the cotton gin, the spinning jenny and the power loom, each of which accelerated production of fabrics. Rather we are here concerned with the effects this faster production had upon the accompanying operations of preparing the fibers and the woven fabrics for their intended purposes. In this we shall find that chemical products are integral with the processes of making clothing available cheaply.

The first step in the preparation of fibers before spinning is to free them from foreign matter of various kinds. Wool on the animal's back is covered with a greasy coating of dried sweat (a natural waterproofing); silk in the cocoon is also coated with materials unneeded and undesirable in thread or fabric; and cotton and linen must be freed from impurities. Each requires careful washing with specially made and chosen soaplike compounds which have the ability to emulsify away non-fibrous materials leaving the fiber clean and pure for subsequent treatment. These detergents, because of the special nature of the jobs they are to do, must be more exactly made and used than any ordinary soap and must leave the treated fibers clean. The most popular of these have been specially made soaps, the so-called sulfonated oils (made by treating various vegetable and animal oils with strong sulfuric acid) and more recently an entirely new kind of soap-like material prepared synthetically.

Soaps, made by treating natural fats with alkalies, have been made and used for twenty centuries. In America, the soft soaps of our ancestors were made in every home by boiling fat with the lye extracted from the wood ashes from the hearth in the lye hopper, long a familiar sight in the back yards of rural communities.

Because the alkali used was potash, the resulting soap never hardened. The method of its manufacture was so crude that the product itself was highly variable in the amount of alkali contained and in its efficiency as a dirt remover. As communities grew, the division of labor required that soap boiling, like many other traditional home industries, be concentrated in factories where a better and more uniform product could be made. Soda was early substituted for potash in this factory making of soap and resulted in a cake which would harden and could be handled as a solid block. Later, it was found that the spent lye from the soap kettles, after the soap had been removed, contained substantial amounts of glycerine which could be recovered and put to valuable use, especially in the manufacture of nitroglycerine for dynamite. This is a typical illustration of a by-product, for glycerine serves no particularly useful purpose in most soaps, but when separated, forms the basic raw material for the manufacture of our most important industrial (as distinguished from military) explosive. Thus, the washing of one's hands and clothing is closely linked with the blasting of ores and the construction of roads, railroads and other vastly important public works through the operations of the chemical industry.

Soap is essentially a compound of an alkali with the fatty acid of an oil having high emulsifying power. Its primary purpose is to allow water to wet greasy surfaces and thus emulsify and remove both grease and dirt. Because of its alkaline nature, soap is not always satisfactory for this purpose and hence other wetting agents whose nature is acid rather than alkaline have been devised. The effect of strong alkali on wool is to shrink it and if the concentration is great enough, actually to dissolve it. The effect of acid on wool is scarcely detectable and consequently acid wetting agents, made by the action of strong sulfuric acid on oils, are preferred for its industrial treatment. These sulfonated oils perform a very similar function to soaps in helping water to wet the greasy surfaces of the fiber and to penetrate them for the removal of foreign matter. The natural waterproofing of sheep, the grease thus removed from wool, is the source of lanolin, important base of many valuable cosmetics.

Just as alkali is combined with fatty acids to make soap for detergent purposes, so also alkali is combined with weak mineral acids in order to make carbonates, phosphates, borates and silicates which have a large place in industrial cleaning. Of all of these alkaline salts the silicates are the most valuable for heavy duty cleaning, due to their ability to attack and emulsify dirt and to hold it in suspension in the cleaning solution without redepositing it on the articles being cleaned. Although the alkaline silicates have been used for this purpose for many years it is only lately that the true anhydrous sodium orthosilicate has been available. The convenience with which this material can be used together with its quick cleansing action and free rinsing characteristics are such that it is being used widely in the laundry and textile industry, in the cleaning of steel before painting and plating, and in a great many other industrial cleaning operations.

Lately there have been perfected processes for manufacturing detergents of entirely new kinds. The vigorous hydrogenation of the acids of fats converts them into corresponding alcohols from which sulfuric acid esters are prepared for use. Naphthalene (the material of moth balls) yields others and naphthenic acids recovered from certain crude petroleums are the bases of still others. The detergents thus made differ from soap in several important ways, not the least important of which is that they can be used successfully in any water, whether it be acid, alkaline or even filled with mineral salts as sea water is. Soaps are useful only in neutral or alkaline water, sulfonated oils tolerate weakly acid solutions, and neither is acceptably efficient in water containing large quantities of dissolved mineral salts. The advantage of the new detergents is especially noteworthy in the textile industry where treatments hitherto incompatible and given to fabrics one after the other can now be made simultaneous.

These detergents and wetting agents are essential to modern textile processing and contribute substantially to the total value of 5 billions of dollars annually of our textile industry's products.

On the subject of soaps and detergents, although rather far from their industrial applications discussed above, it is of special interest to note the growing importance in human affairs of personal cleanliness. It has often been pointed out that a nation's per capita consumption of soap is a pertinent and direct index of that nation's civilization. The chemical industry can quite justly claim to have performed an important function in making modern personal cleanliness possible. As one reviews the past history of this subject, one must be impressed by the fact that every important forward step has directly resulted from the effects of chemical manufacturing improvements which have supplied materials better adapted to the purpose. Among the ancients, oils were used as cleansing agents and perfumes were added to disguise their lack of complete effectiveness. An independent discovery of the value of the ashes of plants and of wood as detergents long preceded their combination with oils to make soaps. The origin of detergents is so lost in the mists of antiquity as to be virtually impossible to discern completely. The manufacture of hard soaps is scarcely more than two centuries old and was a distinctly industrial step since it removed soap manufacture from the category of home industries and transferred it to factories. Although this was a distinct forward step, it was a natural consequence of what had gone before and did not involve the complete departure from precedent inherent in the newest developments in detergents. The modern process of synthesizing detergents of superior quality is the most important improvement in the art of cleansing in modern times.

The people of the United States consume almost $3\frac{1}{2}$ billion pounds of soaps each year. This approximates 27 pounds per person, the highest consumption per capita of any nation in the world. Holland, Germany and England follow in soap consumption but somewhat lower down the scale. The average price which manufacturers secure for this tremendous tonnage of soap is 10c per pound. To make this quantity of soap, over

1½ billion pounds of fats and oils are consumed. The smallest soap consumption in the world is in China where the per capita use is less than six ounces yearly.

The next important contribution of chemical manufacture to textile industry is the bleaching of fibers and fabrics to fit them either for use as white goods or for subsequent dyeing where uniformity of shade would be adversely affected by natural color in the fabric. Traditionally, bleaching was accomplished by spreading linen and cotton goods out in the sunshine, but the accelerated production of the power-operated looms was soon so great that whole counties would be required for bleaching fields. In this situation, chemical bleaches were first used. The earliest of these was bleaching powder made by combining chlorine (derived from salt) with slaked lime. For the better part of a century, this was the principal dependence of the textile industry for whitening products. It had the effect not only of bleaching fibers, but if its action was continued too long of weakening them to a danger point. To avoid this, other chemical compounds are used to render the chlorine harmless as soon as its work is completed. Sulfur dioxide produced by burning sulfur has similar bleaching ability for animal fibers but has never equalled the consumption of chlorine and bleaching powder. Lately, a striking development in the art of bleaching has resulted from the perfection of methods of manufacture, transportation and storage of hydrogen peroxide of high purity. Not only is weakening of the fibers reduced by its use, but the bleaching operation which formerly required a period of time from several hours to a matter of days and much handling of the goods, can be completed with hydrogen peroxide in a matter of a very few hours at most. The effect of this development has not yet been completely evident but it is possible that the result will be an effective bleach at low cost.

Elsewhere, the value of lubricants for machinery of various kinds will be discussed. Here, however, must be mentioned their important function in the operation of modern power spindles, looms, and knitting machines. Such is the tension and friction in the warp on the loom that were the threads themselves not properly lubricated and protected from ravelling by sizes the breakage encountered would offset to a large extent the advantage of the machine's more rapid action. The delicacy of this particular lubricating problem lies in the fact that the thread must move freely in its rapid course and the lubricant must be easily removed after the weaving is completed without injury to the fabric. One cannot, of course, use just any oil for this purpose. Special qualities have had to be developed in soluble oils by chemical manufacturing processes to yield the desired result. Without such lubricants and sizing agents the extraordinary speed of present-day fabric production upon which depends the cheapness of our textiles would be quite impossible.

The treatment of textiles next in importance after bleaching is the dyeing of the cloth. In this field, the service of chemical industry has been most essential. From the few crude natural coloring matters derived from roots, barks, berries and other natural products by simple processes of extraction with water, the number and variety of colors at the command of the textile industry has been multiplied by chemical synthesis until now there are available several thousand synthetic dyes capable of imparting to all kinds of fibers every hue and shade required for every purpose. Brilliancy and variety are combined with degrees of fastness and resistance to destructive forces which meet every requirement and provide Dame Fashion with the myriad-hued fabrics for satisfying every whim.

It is commonly stated that synthetic dyes are derived from the sticky, disagreeable mess of black coal tar. Without further explanation, one loses the wonderful inter-relation through chemical manufacture between the colors of our clothes, the perfumes on our dressing tables, the flavors in many foods, the medicines which heal our illnesses and certain necessities of national defense. One must first understand that none of these important final products exists ready-made but hidden in coal tar. What does exist in tar is a large and varied collection of chemical compounds which are peculiarly active in undergoing innumerable chemical transformations. These crude compounds which can be directly obtained from tar are easily converted into somewhat more complex materials, known technically as intermediates, and these are used as raw materials for further chemical elaboration into an almost infinite variety of other useful compounds. Since aniline was the intermediate from which the first synthetic dye, mauveine, was made by Perkin in 1856, the process and the inter-relation between widely different final products can be illustrated by it.

Aniline does not exist in coal tar but its primitive parent, benzol, is found in the gases which come off when soft coal is heated without access of air. We may then look at benzol as the grandparent of dyes derived from aniline, and by considering some of the simplest dye-making processes, learn its significance. The purified benzol is first treated with nitric acid to yield nitrobenzene and this, in turn, is treated with iron filings to convert it to aniline. Aniline is an oil without color and with very little odor, yet further transformations into which it enters yield a great variety of colors and odors. It is also poisonous but by proper chemical manipulation it becomes the parent of many beneficent medicines. The most direct dye derived from aniline is the so-called aniline black, which is produced directly in the fiber to be colored by oxidizing aniline salt (a water-soluble compound of aniline and hydrochloric acid) with chromic acid. The simplest medicinal substance (whose improper use has brought it into severe disrepute) made from aniline is acetanilide, produced by treating aniline with acetic acid under proper conditions. An odor of considerable commercial importance is that of nitrobenzene, from which aniline is directly derived. From benzol by another series of chemical steps can be derived the military explosive, picric acid, cousin of T.N.T.

It is not possible here to describe in detail the manifold interrelations of the many intermediate compounds from which dyes, medicines, odors, flavors, explosives and poison gases are derived. It will be at once obvious to the reader, from what has been said of aniline, that such an interrelation exists and that having the raw materials and the technic of elaboration ready to hand is an extremely important national asset. What may not be entirely clear is that throughout this wide field, the raw materials, the equipment utilized, the training of personnel, the technic of the various operations and the type of transformations required are practically identical so that having the equipment necessary for part of this industry, one has the virtual equivalent of all. A plant manufacturing dyestuffs requires only insignificant changes in raw material and technic to produce potent synthetic drugs, or *vice versa*. The manufacturer of synthetic odors might easily convert his plant and staff to turn out dyes and explosives or poison gases or medicines. In this field is particularly well illustrated the inherent multi-dexterity of chemical industry, since no fundamental modification is required for changing the product of the plants in this division of the industry through a wide range of possibilities.

This aspect of the dye industry and its correlative branches magnifies its importance to the nation far beyond its ordinary economic value as the support of the huge textile industry and of medicine. In times of national emergency it becomes our essential dependence for many of the sinews of modern warfare. In times of peace, it acts as a reservoir of equipment and technic, and fosters the advancement of scientific research, both of which are vital necessities to our national security. It must not be understood from this that chemical industry is inherently a war-making industry. Far from it. Rather, it possesses and uses in invaluable peaceful pursuits men, equipment, and technic which, when required, can be easily utilized in defending the nation.

Discussion of synthetic dyes has led us far astray from the manufacture of clothing which it is our primary purpose here to consider, yet the relation of the various aspects of the subject is obviously very intimate. Many important facts are yet to be brought within the scope of this chapter. We have already shown how chemical industry's products enter the manufacture of fabrics from natural fibers and how the treatments using them enhance the value of materials. It is now necessary to consider the various processes by which the fundamental characters of natural fabrics can be chemically altered to produce important and desirable effects.

One of the simplest alterations of natural fibers effected chemically to produce a desired result is the weighting of silk, a process which is sometimes wrongly considered an adulteration. Natural, untreated silk, when woven into fabric, possesses a softness which unfits it for some uses. It does not drape well and the fabric is light, both in weight and texture. To make silk more serviceable and more beautiful for certain purposes, the threads themselves must be made heavier and fuller. This is accomplished by making them absorb compounds of tin to a desired extent. Actually, weighted silk is an artificially produced fiber quite different in many respects from raw silk.

Cotton fabrics frequently undergo a process of mercerization which gives them qualities more closely approaching those of more expensive linens. This consists of immersing the woven fabric in a solution of caustic soda and holding it under tension while the soda softens and swells its individual fibers. When the caustic soda is washed out, the fabric retains a greater power of absorbing moisture and a glossier finish. In a very real sense the mercerized fabric is an artificially produced new product differing markedly from its parent, cotton.

Neither of these treatments does more than modify the fibers externally by changing slightly their apparent characteristics. On the other hand, a number of truly synthetic fibers have become important in the textile industry within the past twenty years. In these the initial physical structure of the fibers is entirely destroyed and a new form created which has exactly the qualities desired. These materials, originally known as artificial silk because of their close resemblance to that natural fiber, are actually new products of manufacture which have no true counterparts in nature. They are known collectively as rayon, a word coined for the purpose to remove the unconscious stigma which is ordinarily wrongly attached to the use of the words "artificial" and "synthetic."

There are three commercially important processes used in the manufacture of rayon fibers for the textile industry in America, which, although differing in detail, have the common objective of dissolving cellulose (the fundamental structural material of all plants) and recovering from the solution a filament of the desired shape and size. These methods differ principally in the solvent used to make the cellulose solution and in the treatment of the solution to form the fiber. The viscose process, commercially the most important, consists in treating the purified cellulose raw material (which may be derived from wood pulp, cotton, or other plant source) with caustic soda and carbon bisulfide. The honey-like solution thus formed is subsequently squirted through minute orifices in a platinum plate into a pre-cipitating solution (containing sulfuric acid), which reconverts the sirup into cellulose of the desired shape.

This way of forming a filament is a mere man-made form of Nature's own method. The filaments are formed by the silkworm in the same way by squirting a thick fluid through tiny holes in its head. Wool and hair are similarly formed by the natural process of forc-ing a semi-liquid mass through minute pores in the skin of animals. Curiously enough, the difference be-tween straight and curly hair is to be found in the tiny canals in the skin in which hardening occurs. Straight hair comes through straight canals and curled or kinky hair hardens in curved tubes.

Acetate rayon is made by treating cellulose with the anhydride of acetic acid (the acid that gives vinegar its tang), dissolving the cellulose acetate in an appropriate solvent, shaping the filament through a spinneret and evaporating the solvent. The third variation, the cu-prammonium process, uses a solution of copper in am-monia as the solvent for the cellulose, but in other re-spects resembles the viscose process.

Whichever process is employed in making the rayon, the ultimate fibers may or may not resemble silk in ap-pearance but possess individual affinities for dyes which differ according to the process of manufacture and are different from those of the natural fibers. These various methods of rayon manufacture have given the textile industry new kinds of fibers with which to work and

RAYON VERSUS SILK IN THE U.S.A.

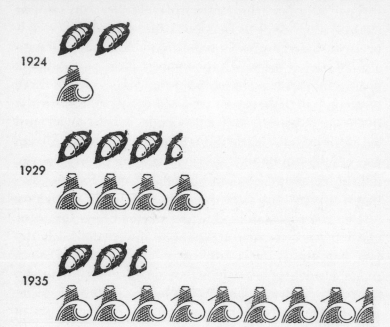

1924

1929

1935

Each silk worm represents 30 million pounds of raw silk imported
Each rayon symbol represents 30 million pounds of rayon produced

PICTORIAL STATISTICS, INC.

have placed silk-like clothing within the reach of all. By using wool, silk, cotton and linen fibers in various admixtures with any of the four principal varieties of rayon, the dyer can produce, through their different affinities for his dyes, remarkably varied patterns and

174

color combinations of which fashion has taken full advantage. They have had the further effect of rendering us nationally independent of silk-producing countries from whom our purchases of silk were formerly important in the international balance of trade.

Since variety is the most important factor in sales of clothing, it is obvious that the value of chemical products consumed by the textile manufacturer, although a small part of his total expenditures, is an essential one. A dark blue suit of clothes for a man may contain three and one-half ounces of dye whose original cost to the dyer was about one dollar a pound. Twenty-five cents' worth of dye has made the suit so attractive that a man is persuaded to buy it. A lady's dazzling evening gown, selling for say one hundred dollars, may contain perhaps ten cents' worth of dye. The conclusion is obvious.

The use of color in clothing makes life a far more cheerful pleasure than it would be if we were solely dependent on the naturally gray appearance of cloth made from untreated fibers, or on the dull monotony of Nature's dyes. The psychological value of color, plentifully available for application to every kind of article of our daily use, brightening our outlooks and stimulating our thoughts and emotions, is essential to modern existence. One need but contemplate his present surroundings to realize how real is the contribution of color to happiness.

In considering clothing, the role of leather must not be neglected. A large quantity of various products of chemical industry is used to make the leather of modern shoes better, softer and longer wearing than that which chafed the feet of our ancestors. Within the comparatively short space of the past two decades, the art of tanning (whose origins date back far beyond recorded history) has been completely revolutionized by the introduction of chemical methods to replace the cruder primitive methods developed before the dawn of civilization. Chrome tanning, based on the use of compounds of the metal chromium instead of the traditional extracts of the barks of trees, gave us an entirely new variety of leather and other important improvements in tanning by both natural and synthetic tanning materials have vastly increased the utility value of leather. It is no longer necessary to hire some one with especially tough feet to break-in each pair of new shoes for us since modern tanning does that for us before the shoemaker gets the leather.

In connection with this discussion of leather, it is pertinent to point out the very important development of leather-like materials, built up by coating fabric bases with nitro-cellulose lacquers and impressing a grain on this finish to give it a pleasing appearance. It is not fair to consider these materials as leather substitutes any more than it is fair to consider rayon a substitute for silk. Both are new materials of manufacture possessing some of the qualities and characteristics of already known materials and, in addition, others of their own which are both new and essentially useful. Developed from the same basic technic as that utilized during the World War in supplying smokeless powder to the armies, the so-called artificial leathers have a wear resistance and a resistance to water far superior to those of tanned hides whose value in footwear, particularly, largely depends on the original pores of the animal retained in the finished leather. Like many other products of chemical ingenuity, these synthetic leathers have come into their own only after the erroneous idea that substitution means inferiority had been overcome and emphasis was placed on their own qualities rather than resemblance, real or fancied, to some natural product. One of the most significant applications of nitrocellulose coated fabrics has been in the upholstery of automobiles already mentioned. The bookbinders' art was supplied a new protective and decorative medium, and the makers of innumerable other articles have improved and, at the same time, cheapened their products with the new material. So important has this development become that the leather industry itself has borrowed and applied the technic of its imitator to produce variety in otherwise monotonous leather products.

The accessories of clothing, too, have profited from the advance of chemical science and industry. Buttons are now available to the tailor and the dressmaker in a wide variety of synthetic and semisynthetic materials. The waste skim milk of the dairy industry supplies casein from which, through chemical elaboration, a plastic is made for the manufacture of buttons which are superior to the older bone buttons. Other plastics in wide variety, both as to external characteristics and ability to absorb color to match exactly the shade desired, are constantly utilized in making buttons and the ornaments of clothing.

HOUSING

Modern chemical industry has contributed to the comfort, convenience and protection of the homes of our people in so many important ways that discussion of more than a few here would be tediously long. In the fabric of building, portland cement, fireproof roofing materials, the modern portland cement stucco, cement-asbestos products, the metals and alloys which have made possible the newest trends to modernism in house design, and the pleasing decoration and protection of modern paints have become vital necessities. Within the house, countless conveniences and comforts now considered essentials rather than the mere luxuries they were a few decades ago are directly traceable to chemical industry.

Even the age-old manufacture of clay building brick has been improved by the contributions of chemical science and industry. The pleasing effects produced by coloring the surfaces of bricks and tiles, resulting in tapestry brick and the originally weathered appearance of freshly made and laid tile, come from the application of weather-fast mineral colors originating in chemical factories. Tile roofs and fire resistant shingles made from asbestos and cement or other combinations, similarly decorated with chemically made colors, give the house builder media with which to convert the plainest designs into pleasingly varied structures by proper choice of decorative materials. The structure of the house, if it be the usual frame type, is rendered resistant to destructive insects and termites by the judicious ap-

plication of chemical products. Over the frame structure, a finished surface of stucco (colored to suit the
owner's fancy) uses still other chemical products made
from the crude salt brines of deep wells. Improved
mortars to hold brick veneers in place for the ages and
cement for foundations benefit from chemical products
which control the time of their setting and their resistance to water and other destructive influences. Damage to concrete caused by freezing, where circumstances
require work to be done in winter weather, is avoided
by using quick hardening special cements and special
concrete mixtures containing anti-freezing compounds
produced by chemical industry. Weather resistant
paints, whose characteristics can be varied practically
at will to fit required conditions, insulation to equalize
the temperature inside the dwelling, and glass to admit
the light of day are among the important features of
housing directly attributable to chemical industry.
Lightweight building blocks, plaster for walls, fireproof
boards and sound deadening walls use gypsum in various combinations.

Paint—pigments ground to a smooth paste in a liquid
in which they do not dissolve—is an interesting and
important story of man's continuing conquest of Nature.
Before the dawn of history the earliest paints were
used for purely decorative purposes to make crude
drawings more strikingly real. Certain clays were
found to possess a combination of color and a vigorous
adhesiveness which held them in place after they had
been spread on a surface. Later, colored pigments were
mixed with milk, gums and other materials which im-

parted still more pronounced adhesive powers, and in the regions of northern Africa where little rain has disturbed them, we still find traces of paintings originally made long before the dawn of the Christian era.

Pigments were early mixed with vegetable oils to help them cling to surfaces, particularly to human skin for cosmetic purposes. The coating of objects with very thin sheets of gold, stuck in place with bitumen discovered in springs in Asia Minor, was so successfully done that many examples of this art survive from earliest times. Herodotus, in his illuminating stories of his travels, describes in recognizable detail the process of making a white pigment from lead which is to all intents and purposes identical with that practiced today in making white lead. Marco Polo found in the Far East examples of lacquer work achieved, we now know, through the use of natural resins, which were far ahead of anything western civilization of the Middle Ages had to offer. Throughout the then known world, the art of mixing clay and mineral pigments to produce a variety of colors was widely practiced, but nowhere had the idea of using paint for protection been recognized. Indeed, this thought, so important today, of applying to structures an easily renewable coating for the principal purpose of resisting the wear of the elements, is a development of comparatively recent times.

The crucial improvement in ancient paints, which has made their modern utility possible, came into being in the sixth or seventh century when drying oils—those having the important ability to harden into a solid layer when thinly spread on a surface—were first used as the vehicle of paints. We do not know the name and can only guess at the nationality of this benefactor of humanity, although it seems probable that he was a citizen of one of the Mediterranean countries, most probably of Italy. It is fairly sure that he used his discovery solely in decoration and that only the accumulated experience of the centuries following led to the idea of using pigments ground in drying oils for the protection of wooden structures from the weather. The idea of surface coatings as protection was already developing in the art of ship-building where bitumen and tars from various trees, particularly the conifers, were used from earliest times to keep water out of cracks in timbers of the craft that plied the waters of the Mediterranean and its tributary streams. The Ark of Noah is said to have been rendered watertight by the application of pitch, and it is questionable whether this was its first application, since fishing from boats was one of the oldest of human occupations. In the meantime, decorative painting had been developed to a rather advanced point by the use of various distempers (water colors) and of solutions of natural resins as the vehicles for the adhesion of pigments to surfaces. The property of walnut oil, and later the oil from flaxseed, to change on the surface from a spreadable liquid to a tough, adhesive, resin-like film, was recognized by artists of the brush soon after its discovery as a valuable addition to the tools of their trade.

Protective coatings, as we have indicated, waited for experience to show that an underlying surface could be preserved by a thin layer of paint spread upon it, and it was not until the development of special need for this protection for the wooden buildings of colonial America that this phase of painting was given the impetus for growth. The early colonists, as soon as their safety and the permanence of their new settlements were assured, realized the need for some such protection to preserve their houses from weather, and the industry of paint manufacture soon became important in the economy of the new world.

The investigative spirit of the late nineteenth century in America put together its accumulated knowledge of paints, and their congeners the printing inks, and showed the way to control and improve the drying qualities of the oils available and to prepare long-lived, weather resistant coatings. Varnishes made by dissolving natural resins in oils were found to dry better and quicker when certain metals, notably lead, manganese and later cobalt, were dissolved at the same time. These driers, as they were called, were supplied at first accidentally, but later in purified form as products of chemical industry attained increasing usefulness. New pigments were developed by chemical manufacture to supplement the white lead and zinc oxide that had been used traditionally. Lithopone (a purely synthetic pigment), titanium white (having a whiteness far greater than any other pigment yet known), special red oxides of iron made from the wastes of chemical operations and having high tinctorial power, and a great number of colored chemical compounds made especially for the paint makers' use have greatly increased the variety and utility of paints. Numerous rust resistant paints, notably those based on red lead, chromate pigments and certain forms of carbon black, have been developed by chemical industry to reduce our enormous annual expense from the rusting of steel and iron structures. One can truthfully say that the only real developments in the art of painting, particularly for protective purposes, since the time of Mahomet, have been the direct results of chemical ingenuity and the application of this knowledge in chemical industry, principally in the United States of America.

Although the principle of the protective coating of property was first recognized and for a long time thereafter practiced principally in the application of paint to wood, the growing use of metals brought disappointing realization that they too are not permanent—that the rusting of iron and steel and the tarnishing of copper, brass and bronze spoiled the appearance, impaired the utility, and finally threatened the very existence of the most useful of the early metals and alloys. From that time to the present much ingenuity and considerable research have been spent in the search for a paint or other liquid coating permanently protective of metals, but the aggregate progress is surprisingly small. However, the coating of metals with other metals has been more fruitful of results, and iron, or steel, has been successfully coated and for long periods protected in chronological succession with tin, lead, and zinc by hot dipping and with copper, nickel, zinc and chromium by electroplating—not forgetting two recent processes of surface protection based on the formation of phosphate films, effective rather than decorative, however. In

both permanence and beauty chromium plate surpasses
its predecessors, and almost every room in the modern
home contains one or more fixtures, utensils or objects
of art made more lasting and sightly by that excellent
protective coating.

One of the most important recent developments has
been the use of synthetic resins to replace those provided by Nature in the manufacture of varnishes and
the vehicles of enamel paints. The development of synthetic resins from phenol and formaldehyde, whose disappointing insolubility in common solvents was their
most valuable characteristic, has been discussed. Later
developments of the same fundamental idea of resin
formation has led to the discovery of methods of making such resins which under proper conditions will dissolve in drying oils—particularly in tung oil recently
transplanted to this country from China where it has
been used for centuries—to yield varnishes of remarkable properties. Other synthetic resins are also used.
These synthetic resin varnishes are highly resistant to
moisture, more so than other varnishes. They retain, in
some degree, the germicidal properties of the parent
substances from which the resins are made and are thus
especially valuable on ships and boats to prevent the
attachment of marine growths. What is even more important, they dry with extraordinary speed. Ordinarily,
the quicker a paint dries the shorter is its life, but this
is not true of the new synthetic resin varnishes containing tung oil nor of paints made from them. Where ordinary paints require days, these new paints dry hard
in a matter of a few hours, and hence they have put in

the paint makers' hands an effective answer to the inroads of nitrocellulose lacquers on his traditional domain.

The story of the nitrocellulose lacquers is one of the most fascinating in modern chemical development and involves the fitting together of a number of apparently unrelated facts from quite different fields of activity. In a very real sense, this industry grew as a direct result of the World War, and even though nothing can compensate for the tremendous cost in suffering and materials of that catastrophe, here is one permanent benefit derived from our part in it.

To begin at the beginning, one must recall that smokeless powder, made by treating cotton with nitric acid, was the principal explosive used in propelling the projectiles from all the guns, big and little, used in the war. The demand was prodigious. Almost unimaginably huge quantities of cotton were consumed in its manufacture and virtual armies of men were engaged in making it. The process consisted in washing the cotton to free it from foreign matter, treating it with a mixture of nitric and sulfuric acids, washing away the acid, forming a paste from the resulting nitrocellulose by adding proper mixtures of ether and alcohol, shaping the paste into powder grains of the required sizes and evaporating out the solvent. These operations, with a number of minor ones, became very familiar to many men and plants of huge capacity were erected to carry them out. The end of the war thus left idle a number of plants, representing large investments, since they were especially adaptable to this one purpose only, and a great many men with the now unwanted knowledge of the manufacture of smokeless powder. Probably those two kinds of idleness were more important than any other factor in fostering the development of an industry to use at least a part of these potential resources.

In looking for some employment for the talents of men and for idle plants, the idea of using their product to make lacquer coatings was early considered, for already there existed a small industry supplying this finish, familiar on small brass articles, as a tarnish resistor. The difficulty seemed to be that solutions of nitrocellulose of sufficient concentration to be worthwhile in forming such a coating had the unfortunate drawback of being thick and jelly-like. That was an insuperable obstacle until one day, in a plant preparing cotton for nitration, the power stopped for a considerable period and the operating force was so occupied that no one realized that the batch of cotton was being long overtreated with caustic soda. Marvellous to relate, that particular batch of cotton which was being nitrated to become celluloid refused to form a jelly when the accustomed solvents were added, but rather dissolved to a honey-like liquid. Spoiled as it was for celluloid manufacture, that batch of cotton was the turning point whence the direct road led to modern lacquers, for by thus overtreating the raw material in the cleaning operation, a resulting nitrocellulose was made which could be used as a paint vehicle.

This is, of course, by no means all of the story. The British, in order to foster the home industry of wood distillation, had included a certain amount of acetone in the solvent specified for use with others in colloiding or shaping their gunpowder. This was a beneficent provision until the demands of the World War became so great that all the facilities then existing in the world could not supply the required amount of acetone. It must be understood that the accuracy of gun fire depends upon the utmost precision in the manufacture of its powder and that any change in the process immediately nullifies the effectiveness of even the most accurate ordnance. Thus it was necessary to find quickly a prolific source of acetone to keep the British guns effective. Many years before, attempts had been made to synthesize rubber from butyl alcohol, a brother of grain alcohol. One of the promising methods of making this raw material was by the action of a certain microorganism on starch. The microorganism had been carefully studied and was found to produce acetone in considerable quantities along with butyl alcohol. Immediately this "bug" was put to work to meet the shortage of acetone in Britain and the problem seemed solved. It was for the British army, but the operators of the process, among whom was a group utilizing an old whisky distillery in our Middle West, had still the problem of getting rid of tremendous quantities of butyl alcohol which had to be made to get the desired acetone and which no one needed at all. This by-product could not be burned or dumped in the streams and hence a huge reservoir—which has since served as an admirable swimming pool—was built to store it until some future use might be found. That use was not forthcoming until the accident in the nitrocellulose plant showed the way to make soluble cotton that would not jelly in solutions of useful concentrations, but then butyl alcohol became an indispensable part of the foundation of the new industry of lacquers for it provided the raw material for a proper solvent to make useful nitrocellulose solutions. It is scarcely likely that the new industry would have gotten off to such a prompt start if the manufacture of solvent had had to be undertaken from the beginning. The stored supply was great enough to give the lacquer manufacturers all they needed, at low cost and without investment, until they could explore the commercial possibilities of the new product.

A third important consideration in the formation of the lacquer business and its subsequent rapid growth was the manufacture of suitable pigments to give the product color and covering power. The lead and zinc pigments, traditionally valuable in oil paints, were found to be totally unsuited for use in nitrocellulose lacquers and it was necessary to accelerate the production of other pigments hitherto less important to meet the new demands. Among these, lithopone, made from zinc and barium ores, and titanium oxide were the most important white pigments. Along with them a host of colored pigments had to be made from minerals or from synthetic dyes that would not affect the wearing and weathering qualities of the lacquer vehicle. These had already been made in some quantity but it was necessary to increase their production rapidly to meet the needs of the new lacquers which became popular almost overnight.

The production of bright and durable shades of pigment colors has been so successful that even multicolor patterns have become popular on motor cars, and the appreciation of the public of these brighter shades has been such that it has been suggested that this has been the main factor in stimulating the color consciousness of the public to a point where even the handle of the paring knife in the ten-cent store is now supplied in bright color.

The present-day nitrocellulose lacquer business is distinctly a creation of the American chemical industry of which it properly forms a part. It typifies to a remarkable degree the multi-dexterity of the industry and demonstrates, as few other examples could, how needs of the people are met by the creation of special products of chemical industry.

The most significant value of the new lacquers is that they combine a high degree of decoration and weather resistance with the property of drying within a matter of minutes, so that in a single working day as many as half a dozen coats can be applied which would have required at least as long as a day per coat with the older oil paints or varnishes. In this, they differ essentially from the ancient oriental lacquers made from natural oil and gums and laboriously applied in innumerable thin coats. The saving in the cost of finishing and refinishing automobiles averages about $10 per car year or a total saving of 240 million dollars per year in one field of usefulness from this one development of chemical industry alone.

Great as is this dollar saving, the factor of time economy is probably of more importance. Indeed it is doubtful if the automotive industry, as we know it to-day, could exist without these new quick drying finishes which also permit satisfactory repair of damages in the production line. The tie-up of capital due to goods in process and the actual factory space required if it were necessary to use the older oil paints and varnishes would have placed a burden on the industry that it is difficult to conceive of meeting.

An interesting estimate of the value of paint as a protective covering, not solely from the economic stand-point, brings to light the extreme importance of this ubiquitous article which enters into every phase of human activity. Some of the obvious uses are the painting of homes, of buildings, of fences, and indeed every structure.

Enormous quantities of paint are used in the protection of wood from decay and of metals especially iron and steel from corrosion. The painting of bridges preserves these complicated structures indefinitely and without the protecting coat it would soon become unsafe.

In factories light colored paints add sufficiently to the illumination so that the employees work with materially greater efficiency and accuracy. There are other psychological effects of distinct value in painted surroundings. This thought is well illustrated by the modern tendency to paint dwellings for working people in pleasant and contrasting colors, thereby making the homes more attractive, which shows an instant effect in the endeavor of the members of the household to keep their surroundings in better condition. The old

habit of painting tenements with dull paint, which gave
an appearance of misery to the houses of working people, has been happily abandoned by growing intelligence.

The conservation of property is paralleled by the
conservation of life. The marking of highways, road-
side objects, trees and fences prevents accidents on the
highways. The painting of hospital walls which may
be easily washed or stay clean by themselves has proved
absolutely necessary to prevent accumulation which
would encourage the growth of bacteria and lead to
serious complications, especially in the operating room.
In a lying-in hospital in a large city, in a given period,
there had been more than 100 cases of puerperal fever,
with a high death rate. After the walls were painted
it was noted that in the similar period following, cases
of puerperal fever had almost become nil. Undoubtedly, paint was largely responsible for this saving of
forty lives. Forty years ago, out of every 1000 born,
240 babies died. Today, out of every 1000 born, only
61 die. The growing recognition and use of paint for
cleanliness and cheerfulness is playing an important
part in saving the nation's babies.

Calculation, though admittedly in the nature of a
conservative estimate, shows that the annual per capita
expenditure for paint products in this country of $4.76
produces an annual economic saving per capita as high
as $28.70. This direct saving on the basis of our present
population is over three billion dollars a year which
must be credited to the use of paint. The great saving
of life through sanitation and safety resulting from

the use of paint (omitting consideration of the beauty that has been added to our lives in living in colorful surroundings) is an extra dividend outweighing these material savings.

WITHIN THE HOME

Light and heat are among the first essentials to make a dwelling of a bare structure. The first is provided in the modern home through the use principally of glass, and hence this important chemical product will be the first of comfort producing materials to be considered here.

Glass manufacture is one of the most venerable industries dating back to the Egyptians and Venetians. Rome became the center of glassmaking, it became the glory of Venice. The principles of production and the method of working were so well developed that no great change in the general processes took place until the end of the last century.

One of the earliest, if not actually the first, chemical manufactures initiated on the North American continent was a glass furnace operated by Captain John Smith's colony in Virginia in the period immediately following their landing in 1607. Sand, potash and lime were melted together to provide glass from which beads could be made for exchange with the Indians. Whether glass was made for other purposes in this first plant we do not know, since this earliest settlement was soon after destroyed completely by the Indians, a poor return for what must have been to them remarkable trinkets. Later, permanent settlements, after they had assured for themselves some degree of security, fostered the manufacture of glass for windows and as civilization has advanced, different kinds of glass have been made and fabricated into a wide variety of useful and convenient articles. The early glass made in New England at Sandwich on Cape Cod is carefully treasured today, both for its inherent beauty of form and for its value as collectors' pieces. Despite the great skill attained in glass manufacture in early America, the most important advances in this art have come within the past three decades. Increasingly varied requirements have been met successfully by the development of new and special varieties of glasses having properties which fit them precisely to exacting needs. Mechanization has made the fabrication of glassware more accurate and dependable and has relieved the strain on the lungs of glass blowers whose breath formerly supplied the molding force employed to shape the semi-fluid melt into the desired forms.

The fundamental materials required by the glass maker are lime, soda ash, salt cake, sand, arsenic and a variety of coloring matters (all of which are mineral in origin) to be dissolved in the molten mix to impart the desired color. Many special glasses require other ingredients, salts of lead, potassium or barium and compounds of boron which replace parts of the original fundamental mix to impart special characteristics to the result. All of these materials are consumed in huge tonnages to supply the window panes, plate glass, as well as innumerable other articles of glass which contribute substantially to our wellbeing and comfort. Recently cooking utensils, even the lowly stew pan, textiles and building bricks have been added to the many essential articles of glass.

The windows of our homes, although apparently admitting all the light possible, keep out the invisible ultra-violet rays which modern investigation has shown to be vital to our health. These rays are freely available to all in direct sunlight. Glass makers have set about to find ways to make their product more completely useful and the result has been varieties of glass compounded especially to permit the occupants of the house to enjoy the full benefits of sunshine indoors. The improved glasses have so far proved too expensive to replace ordinary window panes and consequently are principally employed in the solaria or sun rooms of hospitals and nurseries, where their service is especially significant.

Throughout the history of this extraordinary industry, the manufacture of containers has been especially commonplace. In every household the glass bottle has been a dominant feature. One needs but contemplate the variety of bottles in the household, in the drugstore, in the laboratory, and in general use everywhere to realize that this activity alone is of extreme importance. The necessities of life are being met by the use of many types of glass containers from the most commonplace requirement to the most exquisite and beautiful objects of art.

The lighting of the modern home employs another type of special glass developed to be easily fabricated on special machines to house the glowing electric wires of our incandescent electric lights. There is much more to the story of modern lighting than simply the glass of the bulbs. One must go back to the earliest feeble incandescent lamp to understand the important steps in this long and painstaking development. The earliest filament used in incandescent lamps was a thin, extraordinarily fragile wire of platinum, chosen because even at the incandescent heat of the lamp it was quite impervious to external forces that, under similar circumstances, would destroy any other material. This was both expensive and in some ways unsatisfactory for the purpose. A vast improvement would be realized if some material could be used which would not melt. Carbon suggested itself and to protect it from burning at the high temperature needed, the air was completely removed from the bulb within which it was sealed. The search for a method of making wires of carbon of sufficient strength to hold together under the unavoidable shocks, both mechanical and thermal, to which a light filament would be subjected led all over the world. Finally, a high resistance conductor of carbon was made to serve the purpose by partially burning a fiber of bamboo. These old carbon filament lamps of three decades ago were a long step ahead of the kerosene lamps previously used and whose field of utility supplemented that of the arc lights already in use.

However, the delicacy and inefficiency of the carbon filament lamp left much to be desired. The extremely high vacuum necessary to prevent burning of the filament was difficult to obtain and maintain. The lamp was more efficient as a heater than as a source of light, as too large a part of the energy supplied to it was wasted as heat. In the course of time, the inside of the bulb became blackened by a deposit of sublimed carbon so that the luminosity diminished. The glass of the bulbs was very fragile since it had to be made thin to prevent breakage under the changes of temperature in service.

The question of just what happens within the bulb, which had to be answered before ways could be found to improve such a lamp, were made the subject of earnest study by chemical and physical research workers. Their findings led in two directions: improvement of the filament itself and improvement in its surroundings, the bulb and its contents. Recalling that platinum had certain desirable properties as a material for filaments, search was instituted for a similar metal which was just enough better than platinum to be really satisfactory. Studies of tantalum and tungsten, which because of their similarity to platinum offered some promise of results, led to the belief that they might serve admirably. Tungsten seemed to have more promise than tantalum if it could only be formed into wires, an extremely difficult procedure. Ultimately, a method was found to make the very hard, infusible metal, tungsten, into thin wires required as filaments. At first these were very fragile indeed, little if any better in this respect than the carbon filaments which they sought to replace, and in addition the high temperatures of the light gave them a very pronounced tendency to volatilize (literally boil away) and form black deposits on the inside of the evacuated bulbs. Proper heat and mechanical treatment solved the metallurgical problem of making tungsten ductile and of thus removing the old fragility of the filament. The next problem, that of blackening of the bulb, was solved by replacing the vacuum (inherited from the days of the delicate carbon lamp) with one of the inert gases of the atmosphere, argon or nitrogen, neither of which would affect the tungsten itself but would reduce its tendency to vaporize in the bulb. By thus filling the bulb with gas, instead of pumping out everything in it, the problem of the glass of the bulb could be much simplified since it was thus put under less strain. Special glass to withstand the temperature changes met in use had previously been developed. Now the incandescent lamp has become so sturdy and so efficient that it can be used anywhere.

The chemical contributions to the material embodiment of the incandescent light have made of it an entirely different and more useful thing. The mere addition of inert gas to the early tungsten filament bulb, and the perfection of the method of making the filament itself profoundly affected the lives of all of us. Night has come to seem lighter than day because light has been made cheap and plentiful. If all the light used in 1935 could be made only by the methods available in 1920, the cost would have been two hundred millions of dollars greater—omitting entirely from consideration the even greater value derived in better eyesight and increased earning power of the individual through better lighting.

Special heat resistant glass has been mentioned as a factor in the industry of electric lighting. The story of the steps which led to this improvement and the effects of it is a romance in itself. Despite the growing efficiency and present dependability of electric light, the safety of travel on our enormous systems of railroads has required that signal lights and lanterns use oil lamps which are not subject to the vagaries of a remote power source. In ordinary practice, the heat of the flame raises the glass of the protecting bulb to so high a temperature that a drop of rain may break it, nullifying the safety factor by putting out the light. It was necessary to find a new kind of glass which would withstand the temperature changes inherent in this use. Research ultimately found a glass of special composition which could be heated by a flame and plunged into cold water without cracking. This answer to the problem of the railroads, like all other similar discoveries, had effects in other fields that have been equally if not more important. The most picturesque and commonplace, if not the most important, application of this has been in glass baking dishes and other utensils in the kitchen.

The ancient art of the potter, closely allied to glass, has grown into the modern science and industry of ceramics, whose products are invaluable to modern life. From highly utilitarian stoneware sewer pipe to exquisitely decorated porcelain and china dishes, the whole gamut of baked clay products serves every household. Vitreous enamels baked on iron and steel supplement porcelain bath tubs, sinks and sanitary ware in making homes more healthful and more livable. The notable resistance of ceramic products to destructive agencies, including the corrosive products made and handled in chemical operations, gives a permanence to their beauty in the home and an extraordinary value to their service to industry.

Already, we have discussed the preparation of textile fabrics and the important part which soap and similar chemical products play in this operation. In the kitchen, many of the same types of soaps utilized by the textile industry clean garments after wearing and use have soiled them. The same problems of clean water exist in the household laundry which have to be solved on a much larger scale by the bleachers and finishers of textiles, but unfortunately the reward in economy from applying the same measures to domestic affairs is too small ordinarily to justify the trouble involved. This is true of many modern economies practiced in large scale industry which add materially to efficiency but which, when transferred to a single household, become unprofitable and too expensive to justify themselves. It is on this account that the modern steam laundry, cleansing the clothing of many families, can apply measures to insure the utmost cleanliness and satisfaction which would be prohibitively expensive to the individual washerwoman.

The ancient art of preserving and canning, until recently part of the duty of every thrifty homemaker, is being gradually shifted into an industry which can easily and economically apply all the laws of hygiene to its activities and utilize the latest discoveries of scientists to assure perfect results to the particular hostess on all occasions.

Quick-freezing of foods has supplemented canning processes and has improved upon them by avoiding the cooking which often alters flavors of fresh foods. Corrosion-resistant metals and alloys give the food processor clean, sanitary equipment for his operations.

Cooking and the immediate preparation of food for the table have been robbed of much of their drudgery by two important modern developments. The large scale preparation of staple foods has been largely shifted to the modern industry of foods which is abolishing the time-honored slavery of the housekeeper to the kitchen range, and the widespread use of manufactured gas as a domestic fuel has lightened and shortened the task of cooking at home. The effect of gas for domestic purposes on our modern method of living has been of tremendous importance since it permits hundreds of households to live under a single roof whose actual area would be largely taken up by the chimneys they would require for their kitchens were coal the only fuel available for cooking. Not only can kitchens in cities and urban communities be economically provided with convenient gas or liquid heat, but even those who live beyond the reach of gas mains can enjoy a practical equivalent of manufactured gas through the service of the chemical industry, another branch of which provides carefully prepared gas from petroleum cracking and from gas wells compressed in portable cylinders for use anywhere. The interesting story behind this last development leads into many fields since these

gases are first made to give up many valuable constituents for the chemical synthesis of a wide variety of important products, particularly solvents and anti-freezes
for automotive use, before the remaining valuable fuel
gases are bottled in steel cylinders for use. In addition
to these gaseous fuels more than 12 million American
homes use kerosene stoves.

One cannot think of the necessities of living, as they
relate to the modern home, without being led to the
idea of air-conditioning and the control of the climate
within our houses. Nothing is more enticing than the
prospect held out to us, almost within our present reach,
of being able to enjoy within our doors perfect weather
of the precise kind we choose at all times of year. That
one can create the invigoration of a summer day on
the shore of Maine, the zest of October in the Cats-
kills, the delights of a Neapolitan villa overlooking the
turquoise Mediterranean, or what one will, in the
stifling heat of a New Orleans August or the bitter win-
ters of the Adirondacks, is barely beyond present realization in our homes. Perhaps it is a matter of only
weeks, or at most months, before the key is found to
the last secrets which will make such dreams a reality.
When that day comes, chemical industry will be found
supplying essential materials to add more comfort to
our living, just as it now does, in controlling the vagaries of weather in many manufacturing operations and
in an increasing number of public buildings.

8.

Serving Industry

THE important function of supplying special materials to all other branches of industry, which is one of the most important services of chemical manufacture, has been frequently suggested. Indeed, it is impossible to designate any branch of the great economic machine which we think of as industry that does not consume among its essential materials vast quantities of chemical products. In this chapter it remains to bring a few of these typical services of supply into small compass for closer examination and to emphasize the vital part these products play in our entire industrial activity.

It will be well first to review the effects of chemical products on the universal necessity, power, and its production. Industrial power is derived from three principal sources: steam, waterfalls and internal combustion engines. In its production from each of these sources we shall find chemical products functioning importantly.

Steam power requires two essentials in its production: fuel (coal, oil or gas) and an abundant supply of pure water. Coal is at present the most important fuel in steam plants and its treatment for this use consists merely in removing it from subterranean seams, breaking it to convenient sizes and separating as much as possible of the slate and incombustible rock which is dug from the ground with it. In the first operation, explosives are utilized that are particularly adapted for the conditions prevailing at the place of blasting and for the type of coal and adjacent rock. Black powder is the traditional and long-established explosive for bringing down coal, its popularity with the coal miners depending upon its slow heaving action, in contrast to the shattering effect exerted by a faster explosive. By its use, a higher percentage of a large lump product is obtained rather than dust and fine particles. Within the past few years, pellet powder has been introduced into the black powder industry as a substitute for much of the granular variety. The pelleted product consists of cylindrical blocks of black powder enclosed in a wrapped cartridge similar to a stick of dynamite.

Black powder, however, cannot be used for safety reasons in coal mines in which flammable gases are present, because of the length and duration of the flame produced at the time of the explosion. Special "permissible" dynamites have been developed that have a characteristically slight flame of short duration and a low temperature of explosion. These dynamites are designed as "permissibles" because they have passed certain prescribed safety tests of the United States Bureau of Mines. The permissibles are graded according to velocity and density so that different types are available, depending on the nature and hardness of the material to be blasted. An outstanding American development has been the introduction of very low density, relatively low velocity explosives of this type, so that no overloading of the borehole results. In this way, the advantages of black powder are approached without the hazards present from their use in gassy mines. A fairly recent development also has been in the use of liquid carbon dioxide in special sealed cartridges which are set off by means of a heating element. This device presents a very low hazard from the point of view of igniting gas and dust in coal mines, and furthermore, because of its slow action it brings down the coal in relatively large pieces, which is desirable in blasts of coal for domestic uses. Freedom from poisonous gases, such as carbon monoxide, which is produced in small amounts by the usual types of explosives, is an added advantage.

Aside from the field of coal mining, commercial explosives are necessary to the establishment and functioning of power plants. If oil is used as fuel in place of coal, explosives will still have had a part, since a recently developed, rather extensive use for high explosives comes in the geophysical prospecting for pe-

troleum deposits. It may be stated also, as a fundamental fact, that, wherever large scale construction
work is to be carried on or metal machinery or equipment is to be used, explosives must help to prepare the
way. The mining of ore, the quarrying of cement rock
for the construction of huge dams and of highways, the
blasting of bedrock for foundations, the driving of di-
verting tunnels through solid rock—these operations are
all dependent upon the use of high explosives. The
transmission of electric power is over copper wires and
cables, and explosives make available the necessary supplies of copper ores.

A variety of types of explosives is available for use
in general blasting work. Like the permissibles, these
derive their explosive strength from nitroglycerine or
from ammonium nitrate, which has increasingly been
used as at least a partial replacement for nitroglycerine.
The gelatin dynamites, the semi-gelatins, and the ammonia dynamites are the types most in demand, and
intensive research has been constantly improving the
product from the point of view of uniformity, execu-
tion, and adaptability.

As a result, it has been found possible to control the
rate of detonation of ammonium nitrate explosives by
varying the particle size of ammonium nitrate. Low
freezing and substantially non-freezing nitroglycerine
dynamites have been produced by introduction into the
nitroglycerine of freezing point depressants of various
kinds, the most satisfactory being ethylene glycol dinitrate, since it is itself almost the equivalent of nitroglycerine from the point of view of explosive strength.

205

The production of non-freezing dynamites has removed from the industry what was formerly a real hazard. Mention has already been made of the use of low density explosives, which are of particular importance in the field of coal mining. Special attention has been given also to the development of explosives particularly adapted for use in large diameter cartridges in quarry work. Liquid oxygen has found a field of use in such operations. This material is converted into a powerful blasting agent by mixing it in the liquid state with combustible absorbent material, such as finely divided carbon. Liquid oxygen is obtained from air by compressing and distilling under proper conditions, the oxygen being separated from the nitrogen in the liquid state. The bringing together of the finely divided carbon and the liquid oxygen is accomplished immediately before the blast is to be made and the cold-soaked cartridges are loaded into the drill holes, stemmed and shot quickly. Excess oxygen is used above the oxidation requirements of the carbon to make up losses.

Of certain significance also has been the recent introduction of a blasting agent high in ammonium nitrate and not capable of detonation by ordinary means. This new product makes available for quarries and stripping operations a blasting material characterized by high efficiency and maximum safety.

The research program of the explosive industry has not only improved the final products directly, but has been highly effective indirectly by its improvement of the basic raw materials that are also of great importance to other industries. Sulfuric acid, nitric acid, ammonia, ammonium nitrate, sodium nitrate, nitro-glycerine and ethylene glycol dinitrate are some of the materials upon which the industry depends. Much of the pioneering work on the development of the contact sulfuric acid process in America was done by the explosives industry, shortly after its introduction abroad. The nitric acid industry in this country was revolutionized by the introduction of the process depending on the oxidation of anhydrous ammonia, this latter material itself being a synthetic product from atmospheric nitrogen and hydrogen obtained from water. A purer grade of ammonium nitrate by improved processes is now available, starting from synthetic ammonia and nitric acid. A vigorous research program, in fact, has been continuously prosecuted to make manufacture and use of explosives relatively free from hazard.

Many of the most essential tasks of modern civilization would be impossible to accomplish by the laborious methods of the ancients. Our awe at the great structures erected by the ancient peoples of Egypt, Greece, and Rome is rather at the great handicaps they overcame than at any extraordinary difficulty of duplicating their productions by modern methods.

The crushing of the coal and screening it to size for use utilize alloy steel crushing equipment and special steel screens, in the manufacture of both of which products of chemical industry are essential. Dusting is prevented by the use of petroleum oils or of calcium chloride applied to freshly mined coal.

From the operating face to the railway car alloys and

alloy steels contribute economy to the mining and preparation of coal. By oxy-acetylene flame deposition of
a hard alloy of chromium, cobalt and tungsten or one
of chromium and manganese the worn teeth of the coal-
cutting machine are periodically restored to length,
sharpness, and hardness. In wet mines the pumps often
elevate water in tonnage equal to that of the coal
hoisted, and to withstand its corroding acidity they are
usually made of a high chromium steel. For resistance
to abrasion the grizzly bars and crusher plates are provided in manganese steel, and the screens and coal-
cleaning machinery are best made of chromium steel for
long life in the acid and grit-laden water.

Removal of foreign matter from coal has traditionally been a process of selection based on the differences
in appearance between the desired material and the
other rocks accompanying it. Lately, use is being made
of the differences in specific gravity of coal and the
gangue accompanying it in the earth and processes are
being used which make a more exact separation on this
basis. Such processes will become of greatest importance when in the now distant future the more desirable seams of coal are worked out and lower grades
must be utilized. The use of a variety of floating agents
which will separate impurities from even the finest powdered coals has been studied and will be perfected
against the day of need.

The water supply of steam plants must be purified
to prevent deposition on the heating surfaces of the
interior of the boiler of a fuel-wasting insulating layer.
The methods employed to remove the undesired salts

which form this deposit and which are present in almost all water supplies require several chemical products in substantial quantities continuously. Lime and the soda alkalies and phosphates are the most frequently used industrial water softeners. Certain types of minerals, called zeolites, have the very important property of removing the lime and magnesium (the chief offenders in scale formation) from water passed over them and replacing these by innocuous sodium compounds. These minerals occur to a limited extent naturally, and hence their wide demand for softening water for all purposes, especially for steam boilers and washing purposes, has had to be supplied by their manufacture in chemical plants. The most recent important addition to our list of water softeners is a complex metaphosphate of sodium which holds calcium and magnesium salts in solution. The saving, through the softening of water, of fuel in power production, and of soap and other detergents in washing runs into the millions, if not actual billions, of dollars yearly in the United States and the cost of the softening operation is insignificant in comparison.

The modern trend in steam power generation is distinctly toward the utilization of higher and higher temperatures and pressures. The combination of elevated temperature and pressures mounting higher and higher has placed an extreme burden on the structure of the boilers and their appurtenances. Engineering long ago reached the conclusion that the greater the temperature difference between boiler and condenser, the greater the efficiency of utilization of the heat of the boiler plant. On this conclusion, the modern high pressure boiler plant has been developed until it has now approached the practicable limits of strength of available materials of construction. Alloy steels have been suggested and used in boiler construction and the design of the structure itself has been modified to reduce strains to a reasonably safe margin below the danger point in day-to-day operation.

From the boiler to the condenser of the steam turbine alloys and alloy steels resist the eroding action and high temperature of high-pressure superheated steam. The best superheater tubes are of high chromium steel, and for long life the valve discs and seats are faced with a hard alloy of chromium, cobalt and tungsten. To minimize permanent expansion under the simultaneous influence of heat and centrifugal force—termed high-temperature creep—the rotors of large turbines are cast from chromium-vanadium, chromium-molybdenum, or chromium-nickel steel. Traversing the turbine blades at bullet speed the steam exhibits an erosive effect to which high chromium steel blades are known to be the most resistant. The chemical industry has also offered materials to replace steam in power generation which will permit operation at the high temperature needed without producing pressure so great as to introduce unnecessary hazards. The first of these new boiler fluids was mercury, the liquid metal familiar since ancient times. In operation, the high heat of the fire is passed first to the mercury boiler from which an engine is propelled by the mercury vapor generated at high temperature but relatively low pressure, and the exhaust of the mercury-vapor engine is condensed by giving up its still substantial heat to a steam boiler. In this way, it was demonstrated that the over-all advantage of the higher temperature could be realized by producing power in two steps. Efficient though this arrangement proved to be, certain disadvantages inherent in mercury as a boiler fluid developed. Later a similar method of power production has been devised using, instead of mercury, certain very stable synthetic organic chemical products—notably diphenyl, diphenyl oxide and mixtures of these—in the directly heated high temperature boiler. The equivalent in operation of fifteen hundred or so pounds steam pressure can thus be realized without having a greater pressure than a hundred or so pounds in the fire-heated boiler unit. In applying organic chemical compounds for this purpose, it has been possible so to design the steam part of the unit that it can be run at pressures as high as fifteen hundred pounds without unduly straining the tubes containing the steam. The increased efficiency thus attained is to be had, remarkable to relate, at an actually lower cost of boiler plant per horsepower output than with steam alone.

In utilizing power from steam or other prime movers, lubrication and the reduction of frictional losses are essential to efficiency. The most important facts of the petroleum industry as a producer of fuel have been pointed out and incidental mention has been made of lubricating oils which cushion our machinery and save power. To the casual individual, oil is oil and there is no more to the matter than that. From industry's point of view, literally hundreds of different lubricating oils, each designed to meet a particular set of conditions, are essential to keep the wheels of progress in proper motion. From the thin oil required to lubricate the wheels in the tiniest watches without gumming in the course of long use through many intermediate steps to the almost semi-solid heavy oil required in high temperature steam engines, all must be made with exactness and care by separating and refining the constituents of crude petroleum and mixing them with other proper materials to give them precisely the qualities the service requires. In these operations, as in the refining of gasoline, sulfuric and phosphoric acids, many alkalies, compounds of lead and lately a variety of solvents are consumed in large quantities. Some 25 million barrels of petroleum lubricants are consumed annually.

Electrically produced power utilizes products of chemical industry at every step: from the structural materials of which the primary generators are built, the lubricants which reduce their frictional losses and the agencies for the transmission and transformation of the current, to the vital parts of the motors for doing useful work. The manufacture and purification of the alloys required in generator construction, the carbon brushes which collect the current in the generator, the insulation of the wires which carry it to the point of use, the special steels which make transformers of current in power systems efficient, special insulating oils for electrical equipment, the glass and porcelain insulators carrying the lines and the many parts of the motors which consume the transmitted power to turn the wheels of industry; all involve the proper use of products of chemical industry.

Internal combustion power utilizes the chemically refined products of petroleum as fuel. Industry is more and more turning to the convenience and efficiency of modern oil-powered diesel engines to operate its machines. The reason is to be found in the development and perfection of efficient engines to use the heavy oils from petroleum which cannot be economically converted to gasoline for automobile use. This by-product of gasoline manufacture is available today at relatively low prices and in quantities so huge that it is difficult to conceive that we shall ever be without it; and already methods of producing a similar fuel from coal have been perfected to the point where there is little danger of exhaustion of supplies. Heavy duty diesel engines are finding important places for themselves in carrying heavy continuous power loads and the comparative freedom of their operation from trouble and attention is ever widening their field of usefulness.

Among industrial users, coal now supplies about 52.2 per cent of our power; oil and gas, 37.7 per cent; and waterfalls 10.1 per cent.

It is impossible here to catalog all the many chemical products which contribute to our industrial life for such a list would be a virtual encyclopedia of industrial wants. Rather the remarkable inter-relation between industries through their dependence upon chemical production can be illustrated by the effects produced by the continuing development of what was initially a single enterprise. The perfection of the original manufacture of calcium carbide half a century ago is such a continuing development having the most important and diverse effects not only on chemical industry but to an even greater degree on our whole industrial fabric.

The discovery of a method of making calcium carbide in the electric furnace and of its reaction with ordinary water to yield a highly flammable gas, acetylene, was made by an American, half a century ago. The repercussions of this discovery, stimulating countless others in the intervening period, on American life and industry are even more important today and are still continuing to expand with growing rather than diminishing vigor. Let us examine some of them.

Calcium carbide is a difficult thing to make since it is made up of carbon from coal and the metal calcium from limestone both of which are more comfortable when combined with other elements than with each other. This fact not only makes the formation of calcium carbide a difficult operation but at the same time it gives the compound its important value since in the presence of even traces of moisture its constituents fly apart and recombine to form new compounds, lime and acetylene, with the oxygen and hydrogen composing the water. Acetylene thus made is a gas which burns in air with a highly luminous flame, and because it can be so easily made from calcium carbide wherever desired, provides a highly useful illuminant for supplying light in dark places.

The method of making calcium carbide from coke and lime involves first freeing the metal calcium from its combination with oxygen and later allowing it to combine with the carbon of the coke. It is a peculiar property of chemical compounds that extremely high temperatures so agitate the atoms composing them that they fly apart and are thus provided with opportunities to make new alliances, thus forming new and different compounds. The highest temperature producible is thus used to free calcium from its combination with oxygen in lime and to allow it to re-combine with carbon to form the desired compound. This high temperature is secured by utilizing the electric arc formed between two pieces of carbon connected with a source of strong electric current. The arc is in all respects similar to that utilized in electric arc lights used for a generation to illumine our cities with the single exception that its extraordinarily high temperature is made to play around the coke and lime, rather than merely to yield light.

The first electric furnace was necessarily a crude affair and the amount of material which could be treated at one time was barely enough to show the way and by no means such a quantity as might prove useful except for scientific purposes. It is cause for wonder that the flickering electric flame produced in those early days—long ago in the calendar of progress, but still within the memory of living men—would do anything at all, and certainly no one could possibly have foreseen the revolutionary chain of growth from this crude experiment which later led industry to the use of the highest and the lowest temperatures.

Today, modern electric furnaces which supply innumerable valuable materials of civilization are vastly different affairs, but still they perform ceaselessly the same original reaction. Instead of consisting of two small carbon points made by compressing and heating coke carrying current into a heated space no larger than a milk bottle, they may be as much as twenty feet square and eight or ten feet deep, supplied with literally tens of thousands of electrical horsepower through as many as twelve gigantic electrodes two or three feet square and several feet long. Within these furnaces heat surpassing in intensity any known on the earth, reaching a temperature of more than 5000 degrees Fahrenheit, brings about many enormously useful chemical transformations.

Although calcium carbide was one of the earliest and most useful products of this almost unimaginable heat, the gradual development of its applications has resulted in producing an innumerable host of other vitally important materials. Most significant among these are carbon in the form of graphite, having many important uses; the invaluable modern abrasives for grinding and shaping metals; a long list of metals and their alloys; phosphoric acid used in many ways and an essential of fertilizers; phosphorus for the tips of our matches; and nitrogen of the air in a form available for plant food. These are but a few of the essential materials contributed to man's progress by what may be termed the high temperature chemistry growing out of the original preparation of calcium carbide.

Carbon, one of the most plentiful and valuable of the elements, is familiar to every one in its various forms. As coke, charcoal, coal and soot, it is connected with our customary heating arrangements; as graphite it forms the familiar lead in our pencils, the lubricant in the bearings of our machines, the crucibles in which metals are melted, the electrodes in our arc lights and the brushes collecting or distributing current in our electric machines; and as the diamond it decks the finger of the bride or provides the wearing surface of our rock drills for boring deep into the earth. The electric furnace by its high temperature has also enabled man to convert the less useful forms of carbon into graphite upon which much of our modern electrical power industry and its applications rests.

It is unnecessary here to detail the processes by which the heat of the electric furnace converts hard gritty coke into soft, greasy graphite whose high electrical conductivity adds materially to its value. Let it suffice to say that graphite, once an expensive material found in a few widely scattered deposits in different parts of the earth, has been made universally and cheaply available by this operation and that since it is made by man, the conditions under which it is produced and hence the characteristics of the product can be controlled at will. Not only can one make graphite fitted to the uses for which it is intended but by sight modification through the addition of desired elements it can be given characteristics nowhere to be found in Nature. Its electrical characteristics can be varied between limits by the addition of compounding ingredients, and by the extent of conversion of carbon to graphite as can its lubricating properties and its softness. In this way can be made many useful things: efficient electric brushes for dynamos and for motors operating under the widest variety of conditions, conductors (called electrodes) for carrying current into huge electric furnaces, the tiny carbon particles which in the transmitters of our telephones convert sound waves into electrical impulses, the carbon poles of our innumerable dry cell batteries, arc light carbons of varying characteristics which emphasize that part of the light spectrum desired whether for visibility through fog, the purposes of photography or the creation of vitamin D by irradiation, and countless other equally serviceable products used in equally varied fields. Without graphitized carbon, our telephones, all our electric machinery, our automobiles, our trolley cars and all the countless electrical devices upon which we depend would become dead and lifeless. A story will illustrate the importance of these products of chemical manufacture.

It is said that the reason Admiral Jellicoe during the World War was unable to follow up the Germans and make his victory over their fleet complete was because, as publicly stated, of "poor visibility." This was probably strictly true, though perhaps not in the sense in which the public took it. It seems that the Germans were equipped with searchlights which could pick up and make a target of an enemy at a much greater distance than any then used by the Allies. Therefore Admiral Jellicoe's ships could be made perfect targets long before he could see the enemy. It seems that a few days after the War commenced, it was found that a German had been in London with plans and specifications for a magnificent new searchlight which involved the production of an extraordinary quality of carbon electrodes. When the discovery was made, radio halted a ship at sea on which this German was travelling, a destroyer was sent out and he was captured together with his plans and specifications and interned in England. His plans and specifications were sent to America and the construction of a searchlight in accordance with the design, though intricate, was a comparatively easy matter. The problem of the electrode to make this searchlight effective was one fraught with great technical difficulties. However, within three months electrodes of the type required were in actual production in the United States and shortly thereafter not only the ships of England but those of all the Allies were equipped with searchlights equal, if not superior, to those of the Germans. Much often hangs on little and battles may depend on other things than the bravery of the officers and men.

By adding silica sand to coke, sawdust and salt in the electric furnace, silicon carbide is produced which is extremely hard. It is widely used as an abrasive in grinding wheels and in many kinds of abrasive stones and hones. About eight years after the discovery of silicon carbide a process was invented for making crystalline alumina or manufactured corundum. It is made by the fusion in an electric furnace of bauxite, an ore of alumina, and suitable fluxing agents to remove the impurities. The resulting manufactured corundum, similar in chemical composition to ruby and sapphire, is not radically different from natural corundum, but differs somewhat in physical structure. The manufactured product has proved superior to the natural, another instance where the chemist has improved upon nature. Various other carbides such as boron carbide, titanium carbide, tungsten carbide, and zirconium carbide have been studied and are known to possess hardness and other properties surpassing silicon carbide. The abrasive field still presents ample scope for creative work on the part of the chemist. These invaluable hard materials not only sharpen the tools of the world but greatly hasten many operations in the shaping and finishing of all manner of useful metal articles. They find further application wherever intense wear is to be resisted as in the nozzles of sand blasting systems which clean and polish many articles of manufacture as well as cleaning buildings which in the course of time have become grimy. Tungsten carbide, similarly made, supplies tips for tools of extreme hardness and has been of special service on the tips of well drills replacing diamonds and making borings both easier and deeper. The importance of this development in increasing our oil supply may be vital.

The same calcium carbide which electric furnaces produce and which gives us acetylene may undergo other treatments by which it is made to absorb nitrogen from the air in a form suitable for the nourishment and fertilization of growing plants. This was the first answer to the question of the ultimate starvation of the race through depletion of nitrogen in the soil essential to the growth of food crops. The product of this manufacture, calcium cyanamide, is not only widely used in increasing the productivity of our agriculture but by further treatment and elaboration it yields a large number of chemical compounds important in other branches of industry, extraction of gold, insecticides, vulcanization of rubber and the manufacture of certain synthetic resins.

The extreme temperatures of the electric furnace have also had important consequences in adding to the number and variety of metals available to our advancing civilization and contributing to our rapid industrial progress of the past few decades. In another chapter were discussed the numerous alloys of iron with chromium, nickel, vanadium, silicon, manganese, phosphorus, tungsten, titanium, molybdenum and other metals which are scarcely known even by name to the great mass of our people who utilize them constantly in their daily activities. Their value depends upon their ability to modify in important particulars the qualities of the iron or steel to which they are added. All of these invaluable modern materials owe their production to the development of the art and science of utilizing the chemical reactions occurring in the intense heat of the electric furnace.

Many remarkable stories relate the extreme value of alloys in particular circumstances. None is more striking than the use of 85 per cent ferro-silicon, an alloy of iron with 85 per cent silicon derived from quartz rock, which is capable of reacting chemically with a solution of caustic soda to yield hydrogen gas cheaply. The value of this process was demonstrated during the World War by the fact that both the caustic soda and the ferro-silicon could be more cheaply transported to the front for the inflation of observation balloons than could the hydrogen itself, despite the fact that this gas is the lightest known substance. By the use of this reaction in suitable generators the observation balloons of the Allies were kept in the air.

Other metals proving of the utmost utility are also electrical products made and purified from their ores by different but somewhat related processes. Aluminum is of course the leader among these and permits the construction of light but strong structures for many important uses. Magnesium, beryllium and their alloys threaten to replace aluminum where extreme lightness is required. Tantalum, tungsten and chromium are among the new metals which have yielded to the electric furnace and are becoming of increasing value in special applications.

By a somewhat similar process to that used in making other electric furnace products, new methods have been developed for making the phosphoric acid of our phosphate rock available in more concentrated form which greatly reduces the cost of freight on the fertilizer materials purchased by our farmers. A similar process with slight modification has been used to produce the element phosphorus, which in the form of certain of its compounds is the essential constituent of modern matches by which we produce fire at will and which have freed us from the necessity of borrowing live coals from our neighbors as our ancestors did when the hearth fire went out.

Acetylene, directly and conveniently produced from calcium carbide, was first used as an illuminant. Later

the extreme heat of its flame when burned in pure oxygen suggested what has since become its most important use, the oxy-acetylene blowpipe with which steel is cut or metals welded together with the greatest ease. This instrument in the hands of expert workmen has enormously accelerated the repair, shaping, cutting and forming of innumerable articles from metals. The greatly decreased cost of its operations, as compared with those which must be laboriously performed without it, has contributed in a substantial manner to our industrial progress. Acetylene, too, has formed in the hands of synthetic chemists the starting material from which the most important of our present synthetic rubber-like materials is made, an important contribution of the electric furnace to industrial needs in an entirely unrelated field and to our national self-sufficiency should foreign sources of rubber be denied us for any reason.

The oxy-acetylene blowpipe, or torch as it is most often called, created a demand for pure oxygen which none of the methods previously in use could economically satisfy. Indeed its whole value depends equally on cheap acetylene and cheap oxygen in bountiful supply. The air is the most abundant source of oxygen but its separation from the nitrogen which accompanies it required the development of a new technic based upon temperatures relatively as low as those of the electric furnace are high. The contrast of the highest industrial temperatures making the lowest necessary is here very striking. The process which is now widely used in the chemical industry consists essentially in cooling and compressing air that has been previously purified until one obtains liquid air at a temperature of more than 300° below zero Fahrenheit. This liquid air is allowed to boil slowly and under very precise control so that the two gases, oxygen and nitrogen, are separated in pure form by virtue of the fact that their boiling points are different.

This technic not only provided ample supplies of pure oxygen as intended, but nitrogen was a by-product of the process which could be used (but was not) in the synthesis of ammonia for use in fertilizers and otherwise. It also, and perhaps more importantly, led to a whole host of developments based on the use of extremely low temperatures and of such importance as to constitute of themselves almost a separate branch, a low temperature branch, of chemical industry.

The accurate separation of oxygen from nitrogen supplied an opportunity for industry to utilize the scientific discovery late in the last century of a number of previously unsuspected new elements in the atmosphere and to put them to work for man's purposes. These rare gases are characterized by the fact that they form no chemical compounds under any conditions yet produced, and for this reason as well as their extreme dilution in our atmosphere, their recovery and examination were most difficult. It was not until literally tons of air were treated in liquid air plants that enough of any of them could be had to be worth considering. When this was accomplished even the infinitesimal amounts of each became commercially important. Argon, used now to increase the efficiency of our incandescent electric lamps, is found to the extent of about one part in a hundred in our air. The better light at less cost made possible by the universal use of argon in our electric light bulbs is a gift to the people of millions of dollars a year. Neon, which gives a brilliant red light in the now common electric tube signs of modern advertising, is found to the extent of only one part in fifty-five thousand of air. It is quite remarkable that chemical industry is able to convert our atmosphere into a veritable mine of raw material, but when it is considered that such tiny proportions of valuable materials are recovered from it the wonder is magnified a thousandfold. Krypton and xenon, existing in air in the proportions of one in a million and one in twenty million parts respectively, still await the discovery of applications of sufficient importance to make them commercially valuable.

In the same family of rare gases, helium has received probably more attention than any others. It was first discovered on the sun and later natural gas from certain wells in our own Southwest was found to contain as much as two or more per cent by volume of this extremely interesting gas. It found no particular use until man's ambitions led him to the conquest of the air as a means of travel and here it has been of signal value. Helium is, next to hydrogen, the lightest material we know, but unlike hydrogen, it is completely non-flammable. Thus it has become the principal dependence of aviation engineers for filling their balloons and dirigibles to free them from the extraordinary hazard from fire in the air when hydrogen is the gas lifting them above the earth. The process of recovering helium is in all respects similar to that which yields oxygen from air with the single exception that the gaseous raw material comes from natural gas wells instead of from the atmosphere. Thus is illustrated, in a most striking way, how the chain of developments initiated by the original manufacture of calcium carbide has ultimately resulted in new conquests of the air.

One cannot think of natural gas without being at once led to the subject of carbon black, or as it is more correctly called, colloidal carbon, since its blackness is now much less valuable than its extreme fineness. Natural gas is burned in immense quantities to yield soot and if the burning of the gas and collection of the soot are carried out with sufficient care the product is extremely useful in many ways. The rubber tires of our automobiles have been made stronger and more resistant to the wear of the road by, among other things, the gradual inclusion in them of greater and greater proportions in colloidal carbon until now the average tire contains about four pounds of carbon added to improve the quality of the rubber. In countless other ways, colloidal carbon is useful to us in our paints, inks and other valuable products. Even the Chinese, using methods of making their ink sticks that were old when the Christian era dawned, mix American colloidal carbon with glue by hand to make their standard writing material.

The manufacture of carbon black from natural gas is a wasteful process and can only be economically practiced where the gas would otherwise be wasted. This is particularly significant in view of the entirely new and entirely American industry which has lately come into being for utilizing natural gas and the waste gases of petroleum refineries in the chemical synthesis of a huge number of new and useful products. This new industry bids fair to make its raw materials as fruitful of values to humanity and industry as coal tar has been. Its products already range from valuable new solvents useful in modern lacquers and in dry-cleaning, through new synthetic resins and anti-freeze for automobiles to ethyl alcohol which need no longer be made from grain. The end is not yet in sight in this new and lustily growing industrial infant in its service to the comfort and convenience of man.

It is obvious that many of the links which unite apparently diverse and different branches of industry are their common dependence upon some essential material supplied to them by the chemical industry. One sees at once that paper and rubber makers both buy sulfur although the use each makes of it is totally different. The petroleum industry and the steel industry have a common requirement of vast quantities of sulfuric acid obtained directly from the same raw material, sulfur, consumed in other ways by the rubber and paper industries. Solvents used by the paint maker also form essential items in the budget of the rubber factory. The chlorine used by the textile mill and the paper industry is the identical requisite consumed in purifying our municipal water supplies and freeing the population from the plague of water-borne diseases. Throughout the whole industrial fabric runs the thread of dependence on synthetic products related to the dyes and to the synthetic drugs which so potently relieve human sufferings. The textile industry, as well as the paint maker, utilizes chemically converted compounds of cellulose that are very closely related to the smokeless powder of the explosive industry. The waste materials of the petroleum refiners' cracking stills are being utilized through chemical elaboration to yield: solvents for the lacquer industry, glycol used by the dynamite maker to prevent the danger of freezing of his explosive product, solvents which improve the refining of lubricating oils, and a multitude of other important industrial raw materials.

9.

Security

PROCUREMENT of the necessities of war quickens the pulse of industrial development and each major conflict has had its pronounced effects on peacetime progress. The development of helium as the non-flammable lifting gas for dirigibles and balloons, the perfection of alloy steels of new and valuable characteristics, and the conquest of the air by heavier-than-air machines to expedite transportation are but a few of the important developments initiated during the World War period. But for the urge of military necessity, decades longer might have been required to perfect these and other gifts to civilization.

At the close of the World War chemical industry was

readily able to "beat its swords into plowshares, its spears into pruning hooks" and to utilize its military developments to foster peaceful prosperity. Fortunately for the nation the reverse operation, to supply necessary war materials, could be quickly accomplished should new need arise. In an emergency chemical industry, holding the keys to effective utilization of natural raw materials, the preservation of health, and the efficiency of industrial operations, would join the weight of its influence with that of the whole nation to accomplish the common objective, permanent peace.

Chemical industry is in no sense a fomenter of strife, but rather its whole activity is bent toward precisely the opposite objectives. One of the insistent threats to international accord has been the possession by sundry nations of virtual world monopolies of certain essential raw materials or strategic territories, through control of which they seek to impose their wills upon others. These potential causes of international irritation are being constantly nullified by the activities of chemical industry, which finds ways to increase the capacity of lands to support, clothe and feed dense populations, and to avoid monopolies through substitution of materials or the creation of synthetic products. Two synthetic rubbers made on a large scale from domestic raw materials in the United States tend to free us from the need of tropical territory in which to grow rubber. Sheet steel cans for preserving foodstuffs lined with synthetic finishes or plated with aluminum are removing tin from the category of essentials for which we must look to others. Camphor (made from turpentine) and

231

synthetic ammonia, silky fabrics from cotton or farm wastes and new metals and alloys recovered from plentiful domestic sources, synthetic resins having a utility far beyond that of Nature's products and man-made medicines purer and more effective than the herbs, barks and berries of old, each of these is but a part of the national independence provided by chemical manufacture. Lack of no one of these alone could reasonably be expected to lead to war, but the combined effect of irritation caused by dearth of each might well culminate in conflict. Might, that is, were it not for the fact that their supply is assured through chemical ingenuity to every nation alike.

Chemical industry thus stands as a great bulwark of strength for the maintenance of peace, for its beneficent and peaceful activities can, in case of absolute necessity, be quickly turned into the manufacture of materials without which no successful defense of our country could be maintained and no army could withstand attack in modern warfare. The prodigious energy put forth by industry in time of war calls for the accumulation of vast stocks of materials, the expansion of plant and equipment, the investment of huge sums. The assembly of unusual raw materials, many of which come from the very ends of the earth, demands intelligence, business sagacity, capital and energy scarcely equalled by the requirements of any peacetime enterprise. All of this becomes suddenly obsolete and practically useless the moment peace is declared. This leaves industry with a terrific write-off against apparent profits, with increased cost of upkeep and with quantities of material on hand for which new uses must be found, probably at great decreases in value. No industry can favor war on such terms.

Prevention of war is essentially a psychological problem and quite unrelated in final analysis to the means by which battles are waged. The realization of world peace must necessarily depend on the growth of mutual understanding among the peoples of the world and on the removal of causes of international irritation. To both of these ends chemical industry is contributing nobly. No other agency is so powerful in promoting the economic security of peoples which is essential to international accord. The fact that chemical manufacture may be diverted from peaceful pursuits to the supplying of armies in no way detracts from its essentially pacific character. Rather in its character of economic stabilizer it turns potentially martial operations to the upbuilding of that brotherhood of man, that comity of nations upon which alone can rest the permanent peace of the world.

Intelligent people favor national preparedness because no nation will be attacked if it is known to be strong enough to resist an aggressor. The very fact of the acknowledged supremacy of American chemical industry might well cause any foreign nation to hesitate long before attacking this country, whereas, without its existence, the country would be for practical purposes defenseless after the Army and Navy had exhausted the small reserve supply of ammunition.

Nevertheless, the only chemical products which can rightly be classed as munitions are high explosives,

233

smokes, and the so-called "poison gases." Even during the World War propellants and toxic gases represented less than 10 per cent of the total production of chemicals. In normal times far less than 1 per cent of the total chemical requirements of industry is for these materials, and not 1 per cent of the total number of chemical manufacturers produce them. Here then is a paradox. An industry 99 per cent of whose products go into the peaceful life of a nation and furnish those basic supplies without which most other industries could not be carried on, is at one and the same time through its very existence a powerful influence against war, and a strong industrial factor vitally necessary to the conduct of war.

The use of chemistry or chemical substances in chemical warfare is not new. Probably their first use was the building of fire to smoke out the enemy, then the use of fire for other destructive purposes. Means were devised for throwing fire-balls into the enemy's camp to set it on fire. Fireships were devised and steered into the enemy fleet. Arrows were poisoned. Boiling oil or pitch was thrown upon the enemy who tried to climb the ramparts. Conceivably the affirmation: "Hell is to pay and no pitch hot," had its origin so far back in history that we may safely call it Babylonian. One can visualize a surprise attack upon the ramparts which could not be stopped because of this unpreparedness. Black powder had its place, became obsolete, and is now replaced by other propellants. Because they had never been used before, a shocked and surprised world decried the advent of gaseous materials during the World War. No particular comment was aroused by the fact that bombs were dropped on munition dumps, mines were used at sea, and enemy forts and encampments were blown up by explosives, because these methods of warfare had become commonplace and were to be expected.

Regardless of either the effectiveness or the disastrous consequence of using "poison gases," they will continue to be employed whenever a nation at war feels that its interests will be served by such use. This is a situation which has become an acknowledged fact and can never be controlled by international agreement.

In early wars, and indeed down to the twentieth century, a severe wound meant certain death. It is impossible to measure the suffering which the injured endured when a wound was followed by slow death. Nor can one measure the amount of suffering caused by an infected wound from shrapnel against the suffering from poison gases or from any other casualty. But science, while it has given weapons to belligerents throughout history, has within the past three generations and, especially within the last thirty years, brought into warfare marvellously beneficent contributions. Indeed, chemistry has found the only answer to the question, "How shall we make war more merciful." Through its methods and substances devised for sanitation, armies are less liable to disease; through serums and preventive medicines the loss of soldiers' lives from sickness has been reduced so remarkably that disease has ceased to be the major cause of loss of men and efficiency. Through anesthetics and other means, chemistry has provided alleviation from suffering so as to reduce enormously

235

the agony and misery of the soldier. Through beneficent antiseptics, dangerous wounds can be repaired
and life marvellously preserved. So great is this gift of
chemistry to the world that it can safely be said that
one-half of all those who would otherwise die in any
war are now saved by the invaluable substances chemical industry has made available.

The chemical industry, it is true, utilizes practically
all kinds of raw materials from farm, mine, air and sea,
and derives extremely useful fundamentally industrial
products, which can enter into war materials should the
need exist. No less is it true that the immunizing serums
which save unnumbered thousands from deadly diseases in the course of the daily routine of our hospitals
will be employed in war to prevent similar outbreaks
in the ranks of armies.

Safety of life and property at home is quite as essential as international safety and to this security of our
persons and our belongings chemical industry is found
contributing importantly. The prosaic policeman on
his beat presents no such heroic figure as a contingent of
soldiers on their way to war; and the fireman, to the
casual observer, is principally occupied with passing the
time between needs for his services. Yet both are of
vital importance when called upon to act. Both employ
products of chemical industry in the performance of
their important tasks and both must be fearless and expert in their application.

Modern police departments utilize in their continuing war against crime and destructive elements in our
population the weapons developed for the army in in-

ternational conflict. The latest additions to their traditional service revolvers and hickory sticks have come
from that category of materials which people generally
classify as "poison gases," though none are gases at
ordinary temperatures. The most effective of these
weapons, particularly for the use of police, is "tear gas."
The most commonly used material is chloro-aceto-
phenone, to use its full chemical name, which is related
to synthetic perfumes and some important medicines, and which has the very remarkable ability to
produce a stream of tears from the eyes of any one in
its path. The effect is fleeting, but very powerful. No
eyes are injured, but every eye is temporarily blinded by
a profusion of tears. When discharged in the vicinity
of a mob bent on mischief, its effect is so powerful that
one has no choice but to hurry somewhere else. In special cartridges, it can be placed in such a way as to
discharge the instant a lock is tampered with or a door
opened and thus effectively incapacitate an invader
until the alarm simultaneously sounded can bring the
police to catch him. Such protection in banks and other
places where valuables are stored has proved of enormous value in reducing losses through burglary.

The most important characteristic of effective "poison
gases" (using that term with reservation) is that they
must penetrate and distribute themselves quickly toward their objective. In this respect, they resemble
perfumes. The reservoir of knowledge on which any
nation must draw in the event of war is its industry of
synthetic perfume. Few "poison gases" are actually
lethal poisons. The military objective is accomplished

if the enemy is either totally or partially incapacitated from defending himself. Obviously the protective measures for use against chemical weapons are equally available to both sides. Protection ordinarily is so easy of accomplishment that the hope of actually poisoning an enemy with a gas attack is so slender that modern strategists are content to have forced him to wear a gas mask (a chemical contrivance) and other protective devices which materially lower his efficiency as a fighting man. This can be more surely accomplished by the use of lachrymators (tear gases) or other non-poisonous materials. Deadly poisons exist in military armament but more prolifically in the terror stories of imaginative writers.

The reason why so-called "gas" is ordinarily not gaseous but rather a dense liquid or a solid is the purely physical one that the wind too easily dissipates gases so that effective concentrations can be built up only with the waste of huge amounts of material. Furthermore, gases can be handled only under high pressure in heavy steel vessels which are very difficult to move with an army. Solids and dense liquids, on the other hand, can be readily discharged where desired without fear that a fitful breeze will return them to their senders and they can be easily handled in relatively light compact packages. For these reasons, effective liquids and solids are now usually distributed in the enemy lines in explosive shells.

The fire department utilizes many chemically prepared materials in saving property from damage by fire. One is familiar with the traditional chemical en-

gine utilizing sulfuric acid and baking soda, mixed when
needed, to produce immense volumes of fire-smothering
carbon dioxide gas. The pressure created by the generation of the gas forces out a stream of water also, thus
producing a twofold effect. This type of fire extin-
guisher has been greatly improved by the addition of
chemical materials which make a foamy discharge to
blanket the affected area for a considerable period, and
prevent its re-ignition. This is especially important in
extinguishing oil fires which would be spread by water
alone.

Liquefied carbon dioxide has recently been used with
greatest success in fighting fires. Carbon dioxide confined as a liquid in a steel cylinder, under a pressure of
some thousand pounds per square inch, is released
through a series of tiny nozzles and is thus partly converted to a very cold solid (the dry ice of other uses),
and the remainder to a cold heavy gas. By directing
this stream of gas and "snow" at the fire, not only is
the supply of air on which the fire thrives cut off, but at
the same time the low temperature of the stream so
cools the burning material that the fire is permanently
extinguished. This method has been particularly
adopted for use in places where water would cause serious damage, in confined spaces, and where promptness
in extinguishing the blaze is essential.

Carbon tetrachloride, related to chloroform, is an
important part of modern fire-fighting equipment. It
is definitely a product of chemical manufacture, and is
sold under various trade names. It is used extensively
as a special solvent, particularly in dry cleaning of

textiles where it has virtually eliminated fire hazard.

Perhaps the most important method of preventing the spread of fires in unguarded enclosed areas, especially where merchandise is stored, is the modern automatic sprinkler system. These familiar pipe lines along the ceiling depend for their effectiveness on tiny units of a substance which, when heated above ordinary temperatures, release floods of water to quench an incipient blaze. Some utilize links soldered together with alloys which melt at a very low temperature. Others contain a valve closed by a tiny, fragile vial in which is sealed a liquid which will boil at a slight rise of temperature and burst the little capsule holding the water in check. The service of such devices in reducing our annual waste by fire is almost beyond calculation.

Municipal fire and police departments, in addition to their specific duties, serve as a kind of standing army of each community in times of accident. They are normally equipped to meet any emergency. If a person is drowning, suffocated by illuminating gas, overcome by heat or dangerously imprisoned in a building, these municipal life-savers are ready to administer relief. Oxygen and carbon dioxide for the drowning or suffocated, and acetylene in efficient blowpipes to cut away steel bars are among the valuable tools supplied them by chemical industry.

Many will remember an accident which occurred in Chicago at the time the oxy-acetylene method of cutting steel was comparatively new. An excursion boat turned turtle at the dock and a considerable number of passengers were imprisoned with no apparent possibility of escape. It so happened that the fire department had but a short time before been equipped with oxy-acetylene torches. Promptly called, the firemen very easily cut holes in the bottom of the steel hull and many people were rescued. It is needless to say that this dramatic circumstance had a very immediate effect in demonstrating the value of this equipment.

Safety at sea relies upon the unfailing aid to navigation of lighthouses, lightships, beacons, and lighted buoys warning of danger. The maintenance of buoys, with dependably constant illumination under all conditions, uses acetylene to give light in intermittent flashes arranged to guide mariners. Lights in inaccessible locations throughout the world are controlled by light-operated automatic mechanisms which extinguish the flame during the day and start it again when night falls. This doubles the life of a fuel charge and buoys of this kind have operated constantly for as long as two years on a single charge of fuel without failure.

Chemical industry contributes importantly to our safety in many ways. It safeguards our food and our health. As a great element in national preparedness it warns off aggressors. In war, it can supply the needs of the army and the navy. In peace, it aids the police in preventing and detecting crime, and the fireman in preventing and extinguishing fires, as well as in many other emergencies. It provides beneficent signals at sea, and faithfully performs a service throughout the world in making navigation safe. In a manner seldom realized, chemical industry insures security at home and abroad for the whole nation.

10.

The More Abundant Life

DURING recent years, one of the most discussed ideals
set up to be immediately realized by political maneu-
vering has been "the more abundant life." Naturally,
that phrase has been given as many interpretations as
there have been volunteer interpreters. Their common
theme has been luxury and leisure distributed to every
one in the nation. A high ideal, but one more likely to
be achieved by development of industries than by feats
of political legerdemain! While it is quite beyond our
present abilities to define this phrase in a way satisfactory to all, we shall assume that more abundant living
can best be attained in two ways: by the multiplication
of man's powers to accomplish the work of the world

242

without consuming all of his native energies in the doing, and by providing within his easy reach those things for which he most longs. If the ideal be thus defined, the operations of chemical industry and their manifold products contribute substantially to its realization. It is by no means contemplated that the oft heralded magic of applied science, as embodied in chemical transformations, will appear as a substitute for labor and the sweat of man's brow, but rather that scientifically directed effort will be made more fruitful, as if the effectiveness of human powers had passed through a powerful magnifying glass making the reality as great as its image. By this process of multiplied effectiveness, time and energy are freed from the necessary tasks of securing essentials to permit the cultivation and enjoyment of those non-essential luxuries which adorn and enrich the lives of the children of men.

Already the effect of chemical products as applied to the essential business of producing and conserving food has been shown. So great has been the impetus given agriculture by the effectiveness of chemical fertilization and protection of crops, that a new school of economic thought, based on the creation of wealth by limiting rather than encouraging production, has attempted to cure an economic unbalance by destroying surpluses. The validity of this kind of thinking has so far failed of proof, but the effort to prove it has shown more clearly than could any other procedure that improved methods have multiplied the productive ability of our farmers and our arable lands to a point where both may enjoy leisure.

243

The operation of the National Industrial Recovery Act succeeded in demonstrating effectively that the abilities of men to shape and form the raw materials of Nature to their needs have been undergoing a similar process of multiplication. This, too, has been in very large measure directly traceable to the effectiveness of chemical transformation in making materials more tractable to man's will.

Cotton will serve admirably to illustrate the impacts of chemical developments on both industry and agriculture and the way in which chemical industry's products and operations have contributed to "more abundant life" for multitudes of people.

The growth of cotton is an activity whose development in the United States depended initially on the labor of vast slave populations, and which assumed its important place in our national economy after Whitney's invention of the cotton gin to separate the unwanted seeds from the useful fiber. With ample labor at very low cost, the fertility of the cotton fields was a matter of relatively small moment since more cotton could be readily produced by the simple expedient of clearing more land of its native forests. The growth of cotton's importance in world trade and the freeing of slave labor fortunately were nearly simultaneous with the development of chemical fertilizers which not only increased the productivity of each acre of land, but by the same token reduced the amount of labor required to produce each bale of the much enlarged crop. The same area of land requiring an unchanged number of man hours for cultivation yielded much more cotton to

supply more work for the operators of the world's growing hordes of hungry spindles and looms to make more
and better clothing for more people.

The appearance of the cotton boll weevil, bent upon
the destruction of the products of man's labor in the
fields, called into being another important branch of
chemical industry to destroy this pest by appropriate
poisons and thus prevent loss of the fruits of toil. It is
impossible to estimate the damage that might have
been done had not chemical industry been prepared to
supply the weapons for this war on a devouring insect.
It is not unreasonable to assume that the ultimate cost
would have been the complete loss not only of our cotton production but also of our cotton textile industry.
Along with this tremendous loss of capital and the comforts derived from it, huge armies of workers engaged
in the production and fabrication of cotton would have
been deprived of means of livelihood. A grave calamity
averted!

As a directly essential factor in the utilization of the
huge output of our cotton farms and textile mills, none
is more striking than the coloring of the finished products. Nature's dyes are comparatively few and of limited
usefulness. A few relatively dull colors of questionable
permanence are the best that Nature affords. By no
means are these varied enough to provide the multi-
tudinous changes of hue which the whims of fashion
dictate and which so greatly encourage the use of
fabrics. The synthetic dyes of the chemical industry
give an otherwise impossible variety of hue and shade
to our garments and their manufacture is not subject

to the changes and chances of sun and weather which still control Nature's production schedules. By the use of colors, the demand for textile products is fostered far beyond what it would be if only gray cloth were to be had, and as has been pointed out in a preceding chapter, their manufacture insures the continuity and permanence of our manufacture of drugs vitally important to the nation's health.

One of the problems which early arose with increasing cotton production was the vexing question of disposing of mountains of accumulated seed. The solution was reached by the utilization of the seed by and through chemical transformations. The oil which could be readily pressed from the seed supplied certain needs of the soap makers who by the treatment of raw oil with alkali produce glycerine used in the manufacture of dynamite to blast out ores from which metals and other valuable products are recovered. By another chemical transformation, the tendency of cottonseed oil to become rancid was and is overcome by a process of adding hydrogen to it, called hydrogenation. This process yields a semi-solid, plastic, edible fat which is much more useful in cooking and baking and has much better keeping qualities than the original oil.

The residue of the cottonseed, after the removal of the oil, is useful as a fertilizer material, restoring to the soil much of the fertility removed by the cotton crop, and as a feed. As a by-product of the utilization of cottonseed, large quantities of linters (cotton fibers left on the seed by the gin, but too short for use by the textile industry) are recovered. These are admirably adapted to the use of chemical industry in the manufacture of the synthetic fibers of rayon, the useful plastics of the celluloid type, and the nitrocellulose used in quick-drying lacquers and in smokeless powders.

These industries for the chemical elaboration of cellulose were initiated originally with the intention of using these relatively useless short cotton fibers as their principal raw material, but in the course of their development, it soon became evident that the supply available was insufficient to meet their growing need without seriously advancing costs. To make up the deficiency of cellulose, wood pulp similar to that made for paper manufacture is now largely used and other growing plants are being studied as supplements to this abundant source of cellulose.

The rayon industry provides fibers from which silk-like clothing is made cheaply available to all. The nitrocellulose lacquer industry has materially cheapened painting, particularly of the multitudes of manufactured articles which form so large a part of our accustomed environments. From the two closely related activities of rayon and lacquer manufacture has sprung the new industry of transparent sheet cellulose, which protects many of the articles we buy with a glassy sheet from the time and place of their manufacture until they reach us ready for use.

The obvious conclusion to be reached from this short summary of the chemical aspects of our cotton crop is that through the operation of chemical processes this plant has formed the basis of numerous activities furnishing desired useful materials and engaging the labor of many men. It is, of course, true that fewer persons are today employed in the fields per bale of cotton grown, but it is also true that the vastly increased number of bales required, because cotton can be cheaply produced, offsets this tendency to reduced employment. The manifold operations into which cotton goes have created a breadth of employment in jobs otherwise non-existent far in excess of any possible reduction in the numbers of people working in cotton textile mills by the introduction of modern labor-saving devices. Not only has employment been spread by these developments, but the labor required of persons has been enormously lightened as the drudgery has been taken over by machines. In this way, people have not only been given employment at lighter tasks with greater opportunities for leisure and enjoyment, but at the same time means for enjoyment and comfort have been created.

What has been said of cotton is true of practically every industrial activity of our people. Scientific methods utilizing products and processes of chemical manufacture are everywhere lightening the tasks of workers and increasing their leisure to enjoy the products of their labors.

In this situation, the utilization of leisure becomes the real problem. The natural sciences have created the opportunity but its advantageous use is necessarily a matter of mind rather than of materials. Psychology must ultimately solve the problem of the proper use of freedom from toil—but it has not yet done so. Our people must be taught how to live and to enjoy the material comforts and conveniences already bountifully at their command. The cultivation of the fine arts, literature, music, drama, painting, sculpture, must become integral in the lives of a people which has not yet forgotten the stern struggle of its pioneer forefathers to wrest a bare existence from the wilderness. In this modern age when communication over continents and seas is so swift that audiences of millions for the printed or spoken word are reached as a matter of daily routine, the burden of producing words or pictures worthy of such wide dissemination is not yet worthily borne. The molding, nurturing and stimulating of the minds of men to high thoughts and noble actions to be given to the whole world have been neglected, while creature comforts and material progress have usurped the place of human ideals. The creations of science are powerless to alter in any particular the thought imposed on them by their human masters. The silly inanities of blatant advertising of new patent medicines are carried to the remote parts of the earth with no greater ease than the sublime harmonies of Wagner and Beethoven, but the entrance of the two to the mind of the listener is a vastly different matter. The transmission of thought over thousands and thousands of miles is a myriadfold less difficult than the short journey from a man's eyes or ears to his brain. For this problem, chemical industry and science have no solution. Their tasks are done when the material obstacles to the "more abundant life" have been removed. Mental obstructions are being slowly removed by education, but it is a desperately slow operation.

The key to more abundant living lies not in political or economic hocus pocus, but in hard work undertaken and carried on in the light of scientific research. Like the key to the future, that to more abundant living is scientific achievement correlated with a broad public education.

More abundant living has a psychological aspect as well as an economic one. The niceties of existence are realized only in a pleasing environment created by an appeal to the senses. Sense impressions profoundly influence mental outlook and are essential attributes of luxury. Pleasurable sensations must thus be considered correlative with creature comforts and leisure to enjoy them. Even though the means to this end have frequent utilitarian applications, we may properly discuss them here as the *sine qua non* of the beauty of living.

The important contribution of chemical industry to our sense impressions has already been suggested. Hearing is catered to by modern communication, which includes carrying the sublime strains of the finest music into every remote corner of the earth. Visual impressions are heightened by chemically produced colors, which record the fleeting impressions of great artists for all to enjoy. The workaday modern necessity of artificial lighting lengthens our days far beyond Nature's allotment of sunshine. Our sense of touch receives its due share of this industry's attention in the luxurious surroundings which it everywhere makes possible for our enjoyment in fine materials with which we have daily contact.

If the gateway to the soul is through the senses, then

surely that to the subconscious mind, whose importance is receiving continually greater emphasis in modern psychology, is in part through the senses of smell and taste. Unbelievably sensitive, even in modern man whose conscious effort has been to submerge, rather than to exercise and utilize them as his savage forebears did, the nose and the palate rank far ahead of the most refined instruments of precision yet developed in their ability to detect and to identify infinitesimally small traces of odorous and savory materials. Indeed, the extreme delicacy of our olfactory organs in recognizing substances in the most dilute mixtures has been one of the important factors in determining the maximum dimensions of the tiniest particles of matter which chemists call molecules. One has but to recall the ease with which the presence of a skunk many miles away is detected on a still evening and to calculate the number of cubic miles of air through which a thimbleful of its scent has been distributed, to realize the extreme sensitivity of the untrained human nose. This ability to recognize odors was once the principal warning our remote ancestors had of the approach of friends or foes whose aroma was far less evident than that of a skunk. Not only was the nose the reliance of savages to detect approaching enemies, but even more importantly it guarded the body against the introduction of unfit foods.

These primal uses of the nose have been submerged by an advancing civilization which has replaced them by innumerable other safeguards, considered more dependable. They survive in the wild animals which were primitive man's companions and enemies, and even more significantly in the backgrounds of men's minds today. Nothing can so strongly conjure up in the mind's eye scenes that have passed and sensations enjoyed as the chance whiff of an old familiar odor. In the subconscious mind, innumerable impressions, grave and gay, are stored away to be brought out into consciousness only by an odor associated with the original experience.

This thought leads to the conclusion that the reason one chooses a particular occupation or environment may very well be actually dependent upon one's liking for an odor or odors associated therewith. The sailor's love of the sea is in no small part made up of his innate longing for the odors that cling to ships and the tang of the salt breeze. The scent of leather and of horses forms a perhaps unconscious, but nevertheless important part of the enjoyment of the horseman. The aroma of a wood fire is the significant part of a camper's delight, and none can resist the fragrance of pines, firs, and spruces in the forest. The odor of sanctity which clings to old churches is more than a mere figure of speech and it is certainly not beyond imagining that the worshipper's devoutness is emphasized in surroundings of the proper odor. It has even been asserted that the blind are often able to recognize people and places more surely by the aura of scent which surrounds them and which is individualized to the nose made sensitive by the suppression of other senses. Nor is it beyond belief that the devotion of a dog to his master is principally based on delight in his particular scent.

Strangely enough, science, while recognizing the potency of our sense of smell, has not yet satisfactorily classified and catalogued the many varieties of odors that we recognize. No language yet exists to describe aromas accurately except by association with their recognized sources. The precise languages of color and of sound which describe minutely the slightest differences in nuance, have no counterpart for exactly identifying smells. Hence, each individual must depend upon his own impressions in describing the sensations of taste and smell, which in the final analysis are practically identical. This naturally leads to much confusion, for no two persons are affected in precisely the same way and even a single individual's impressions may vary at different times and under different circumstances.

Unlike other activities of the chemical industry where progress has been based upon precise classification and identifying description of the material handled, the art of perfumery and of odors has been very highly developed as an empiric art rather than as a strictly scientific study. Nothing is more evanescent than the scent of a flower whose life is a matter of hours or at most, days, the riotous hues of the autumn woods or the brilliance of the rainbow, and it is these things so important in our accumulated sense impressions that synthetic perfumes and man-made colors seek to preserve. In dealing with such fugitive things, the scientist must of necessity become an artist, and the chemical manufacturer a weaver of dreams to enable them to recreate the fleeting sensations of nose, palate and eye.

The wonder is that such things can be accomplished

at all and especially through the use of what seem to be the foulest kinds of raw material, coal-tar and crude petroleum. Yet it is from these two sources that the constituents of our rarest perfumes and aromas come. Nature utilizes the sunshine, the air and the earth as raw materials for creating myriad perfumes, but so intricate are her processes (intricate perhaps because of their very simplicity) that man cannot follow precisely in her footsteps. Rather, he must learn first what is actually responsible for the effect he desires and follow back along the trail until he finds a familiar raw material. This procedure has been followed with hundreds of sweet aromas until the synthetic perfumes are capable of yielding through skillful blending a wonderful variety of pleasing odors. The common error regarding synthetic perfumes is in mistakenly believing that natural products can be duplicated exactly. This is seldom, if ever, possible and the explanation lies in what has already been said above of the extraordinary sensitivity of our noses which can readily detect differences in aroma caused by infinitesimal amounts of substances no other means will detect. It is obvious that very few indeed of Nature's odors are associated with pure chemical compounds, but rather that each is made up of a mixture of many odorous materials contributing proportionate shares to the medley which pleases us. For this reason, the creations of the synthetic chemist can only approach the natural odor because they are actually too pure, lacking oftentimes the faint overtones which give the scent its character.

The manufacture of synthetic odors and flavors is

not a large industry, nor does it employ vast numbers of people. Its principal claims to recognition and attention are its esthetic contribution to our happiness and enjoyment through the fundamental senses of smelling and tasting—to which incidentally it has given many new impressions not to be found in Nature—and its intimate relations with several other vitally necessary industries. The production equipment and personnel of the industry of synthetic odors and flavors can readily turn out a variety of medicinal compounds, a number of dyestuffs and certain chemicals called "poison gases" essential to our police in times of peace and to our army in national emergency.

The fabulous cost of many of the rarest flower perfumes places them far beyond the reach of the average person who is no less entitled to the enjoyment of their fragrance than the wealthy. By approaching as closely to a natural odor as possible in a man-made mixture of scented materials and then adding a modicum of flower essence, remarkably fine perfumes can be built up, which are cheap enough to be within the reach of all. In fact, so expert are the blenders of odors in their art, that it is seldom possible today to buy at any price a perfume entirely free from synthetic ingredients. Nor should one think of this as in any way sophistication or adulteration. Quite the contrary. Synthetic materials impart their special properties to perfumes and flavors and when properly used, increase rather than diminish the value of the product.

From time immemorial perfumes have given pleasure to man, and allure to woman. This primitive urge of the female of the species to make herself attractive to her mate, present or prospective, is deep rooted in the evolutionary scheme and is practiced alike in palaces and in hovels throughout the habitable world. So strong is the attractive force of fragrant odors that within a very few years claims were put forward, albeit without full substantiation, for a certain perfume that a drop of it behind each of a woman's ears would irresistibly draw to her all males within nose-reach! A boon perhaps, to the Amazon if advertising were only always true!

The perfumes, of course, have been abused and it may be well to quote a curious law passed during the reign of George III, in 1774 as follows: "All women, of whatever age, rank, profession or degree, whatever, virgins, maids or widows, that shall from and after this act impose upon, seduce and betray into matrimony any of His Majesty's subjects by the use of *scents,* paints, *cosmetics, washes,* artificial teeth, false hair, Spanish wool (impregnated with carmine and used to this day as a rouge), iron stays, hoops, high-heeled shoes or bolstered hips, shall incur the penalty of the law now in force against witchcraft and like misdemeanors, and that the marriage, upon conviction, shall stand null and void."

The influence of odors in attracting or repelling has of recent years come to be a most potent force in other fields than in the choice of a mate. Innumerable articles of manufacture carry with them characteristic odors, not always pleasant, which seriously influence purchasers. Rubber has a notably disagreeable odor inherent in the process of vulcanization; paint fills the house with its smell even though very little of it be used; cotton cloth has a characteristic odor until laundered. These, like hundreds of other industrial odors, have acted as deterrents to the sale of the products. The latest innovation to which the chemical industry of synthetic odors has been a party has had for its aim the displacing or modification of these inherent smells by the use of specially designed synthetic odors so that the scent of the products can be made attractive instead of repellant to purchasers. This movement, exemplified in the time-honored custom of scenting glue, paste and mucilage and in the more recent re-odorization of rubber and leather articles, has proved its value and is gaining ground in many industries.

Perhaps the most extraordinary use of an odor either to cover or imply danger was found during the World War where the camouflage gas, butyl mercaptan, which is the chief perfume component of the skunk's bouquet, was deliberately used to deceive the enemy and to cause him either to retire or at least to wear his gas mask and thus reduce his fighting efficiency. He could never know whether this unpleasant smell was used to mask some deadly gas or not. Our own troops, knowing the fact, could advance fearlessly without being handicapped by gas masks as they were informed as to whether the odor contained a killing gas or not.

The importance of chemically prepared insecticides in saving this world from the dominance of insects has

257

been stressed. Another chemical attack on the problem has lately come much to the fore. Odors have even more profound effects on insects than they do on man and the higher animals, and this fact is being more and more used to drive them away or to lure them to their destruction. Pennyroyal has long been known to repel mosquitoes and flies, as do oil of citronella and certain other natural odors. However, the repelling powers of these odors are often far less potent in driving away insects than other odors are in attracting them. The direct flight of bees between their hives and the flowers on which they feed is proverbial, and like many other strange phenomena of nature, it depends almost entirely on the sense in bees which corresponds to our sense of smell. Utilizing this fact, methods of control of insects have been devised which depend on the use of odors which act as baits to attract them. These are selective to an extraordinary degree and a different bait must be used for each type of insect to be attracted. The cotton boll-weevil, for instance, will fly for miles to get at certain chemical compounds, called amines, having odors resembling that of the cotton plant. When the weevils have collected on the bait, it is a simple matter to destroy them. In the same way, astoundingly large numbers of Japanese beetles have been caught in a trap baited with geraniol, the principal constituent of the odor of geranium. Further investigations along these lines are proving extremely fruitful in revealing baits of enormous potency in luring insects from whole countrysides into traps awaiting them.

When we speak of luxuries, the mind instantly reverts to the jewels of royalty, the gems of the Maharaja and the oriental potentates. Luxuries of today, however, frequently become the necessities of the next generation. This tendency has been extremely accelerated during the last half century of progress. Synthetic rubies and sapphires and other precious and semi-precious gem stones are now produced by chemical industry at relatively nominal cost, and their only defect is their perfection. Here chemistry has outdone Nature. The watches and fine mechanisms of the world requiring the utmost precision are supplied with synthetic jewelled bearings which can now be had at prices which make them widely available. The high temperature produced by burning oxygen and acetylene in the proper proportions furnished the key. The question of the production of the diamond still defies the most ingenious efforts of man. The difficulty in making a diamond from carbon is our inability to produce carbon in a liquid state and allow it to crystallize over long periods. We have succeeded in liquefying carbon under extremely heavy pressures but the difficulty of holding liquid at 6000 or 7000 degrees Fahrenheit under tons per square inch pressure has so far defied man's ingenuity.

Among the luxuries of the world which are a direct outgrowth of chemical production is an enormous list of cosmetics and toilet luxuries, the face powder, the lip-stick, the creams, and the hundred other things now so essential to the happiness of the women in every civilized country. The tooth powder, the antiseptic gargles, and even the toothbrush, which is still a luxury in large parts of the world, must be included. The beautiful enamelled boxes, the exquisite bottles, the comb, the brush, and the mirror are products of synthetic chemistry and the remarkable chemical mixture known as glass. One could go on indefinitely but the point is clearly illustrated that luxuries and necessities are becoming synonymous and chemical industry is bringing luxuries of life within the reach of all.

11.

The Crystal Reveals

WHEN one departs from the past and present to embark upon the future, it is common practice to throw discretion to the winds and give the imagination free rein. Never is that temptation so great as when considering the future as it may be predicated upon the swift strides of science, for in the lexicon of science there is no word meaning "impossible." It is quite unnecessary to be led astray by imagination's will-o'-the-wisp to feel that a very wonderful future lies just ahead for the human race through the continued progress of chemical industry. This discussion will be confined to more or less imminent potentialities and by examining recent trends and projecting them a little way into the future, it is hoped that this prophecy may be entertaining and perhaps enlightening.

Improvement in health has taken two distinct trends recently enough to assume that they will continue into the future. The great plague diseases, if one may so designate maladies which affect great sections of the population simultaneously, are rapidly approaching extinction, and the common diseases of childhood and youth have been practically conquered. Epidemics no longer decimate the populations of vast areas, thanks to the modern art of antisepsis made possible by efficient germicides and prophylactics. As smallpox, yellow fever and typhoid fever have now became relatively rare diseases instead of scourges of nations, so may we expect tuberculosis, already demonstrated to be conquerable, influenza, pneumonia, the common cold and other infectious diseases of mature persons to disappear within a decade or two. The diseases of childhood have already been so far conquered that barely two, scarlet fever and infantile paralysis, remain to exact extravagant toll, and these may be expected to join diphtheria among the specters of the past which no longer haunt our young children.

Closely related to these medical advances in which chemical industry will play an important part are the questions of food and nutrition, to which it has already made signal contributions. While biologists are developing species of edible plants which, through generations of selection, will become especially rich and prolific sources of the essential vitamins, chemistry and chemical industry are adopting the more direct method of actually synthesizing these rare compounds from common materials to make them readily and cheaply available to all for addition to any desired diet. The ultimate effect of this movement is already foreshadowed in the vastly improved health and well-being of children not yet in their teens whose early dietaries have been provided by careful mothers with special consideration to vitamin constituents. It is certainly within easy vision that the hearty robustness of the rising generation will excel any of its forebears and that its progeny will approach, at least from the physical point of view, the race of supermen of whom visionaries have for ages dreamed.

Increasing knowledge of the functions of the glands of the human body has so far led to the correction of bodily ills and maladjustments largely through surgical treatments. The more careful and complete study of these chemically controlling governors of our body functions is already pointing in the direction of their synthesis. It is barely a step from the present stage of progress in this direction to the day when media will be plentifully available for the practice of a medical technic yet to be developed whereby glandular disorders will be corrected not by surgery but by the administration of new synthetics to control the glands as the glands control the human body.

Within the present century, the operation of all of these factors has already led to a distinct lengthening of the average span of life. For white men, the increase has been eleven years and for white women, twelve years since 1900. This has been accomplished principally by markedly reducing the rate of mortality in early years so that a substantially larger proportion of children live through infancy and adolescence to manhood and womanhood. This increase in the average life expectancy at birth and in early years has been accompanied by an increase in the death rate from diseases of maturity and middle life. The problems posed by this situation in the control of cancer and diseases of the heart are receiving the most serious study, and if the past accomplishments of the combined forces of medical research and chemical developments are any criterion, it is decidedly not too much to expect the conquest of these now bafflingly abstruse maladies within the lifetimes of many now mature.

While medicine is so valiantly fighting to destroy the diseases of middle life, nutrition is finding ways through selection of diet to postpone by many years the coming of senescence and to hasten the arrival of maturity in individuals. In the aggregate, the combined result of all these beneficent forces is to increase the span of useful life of men and women and to free them from the fears of disease and death.

Not only is the beneficent quality of our food being constantly improved to adapt it better to the sustenance of the race, but recent researches are opening the way for the growth of food crops without customary soil. The new technic has been developed to the point of permitting crops to be grown in artificial light, which can be controlled to give maximum production in minimum time free from the idiosyncrasies of the seasons, in a nutrient solution of precisely the proper concentration of the essential plant foods. The importance of this development, likely to become commercial within a short time, cannot be overemphasized. By providing optimum temperature at all times, light in regulated doses to give fastest growth, fertility in water in a form which avoids any waste, and even the best concentration of carbon dioxide in the atmosphere to promote the photosynthesis of needed compounds, this indoor controlled crop production approaches the efficiency of an industrial operation by avoiding the lavish wastes of Nature. How important this method of growing food may become, no one can yet guess. The possibilities which it suggests of an agriculture based on a totally synthetic environment in which light, heat, and nutrition are supplied as needed entice one to look forward to the day when our food supply will be produced independent of weather and free entirely from ravages of insect and other pests, and when city blocks will serve the purposes now requiring vast rural acreages.

Scientists of the Department of Agriculture, and others, have already obtained extremely interesting results on the germination of seeds and growth of plants when a rainbow or spectrum is used to illuminate them instead of mere white light. It is not meant to imply that the farm of the future will probably be covered with a blue or a red or a yellow canopy, but the study of the effect of radiation on plant growth will prove of importance.

The next step beyond this controlled growth of plants of familiar or new kinds will probably be the carrying out of the actual process of photosynthesis of green leaves as a factory process. The synthesis of chlorophyll, essential to Nature's process, is easily within vision now and the application of this material to the industrial production of starches, sugars, and cellulose from carbon dioxide and water can be expected as the next logical development in food production. Already sugar-like materials have been synthesized in tiny quantities in research laboratories but the adaptation of these processes to the economical production of agriculture's prime products on a factory scale is yet to be accomplished. Probably when this is realized the efficiency of the operation will be far greater than that of the processes by which plants accomplish the same end.

Geneticists confidently make the prediction that we shall be able to grow plants to order. The rapid development of the use of x-rays and the knowledge of genes and chromosones foreshadow the time when the manufacturer will specify the physical or chemical property he desires in his raw material and the plant breeder will create a plant that has it.

With plants, geneticists have already succeeded in crossing two totally unrelated plants. Superficially regarded, the result was a plant monstrosity of no practical use, but actually it was proof to the scientific world that man's skill in the field of plant breeding has reached a point where the most revolutionary developments may be expected before another generation grows to adulthood.

In these ways, chemical industry is contributing a giant's share to what may be called the vital force of the race; but not content with the mere prolongation of life for life's sake, it is continuing to make the lives it prolongs more fruitful through its important influences on all human activities. We have already seen its valuable aid to the transportation of men and their goods over vast spaces and of the thoughts of the great (and sometimes of the very small) minds of the race over tremendous reaches of both time and space. In both of these fields, progress based in large part on its contributions of new materials for the development of new methods has been unbelievably swift. Our world has been shrunk from the vastness of a whole universe to an area over which a single person's voice can be readily heard and which may be traversed from end to end in the short space of a few days. It is only with difficulty that one can imagine further shrinking of the dried pea upon which we now live. The conquest of the rest of our universe still presents problems which prevent any but the most romantic of dreamers from venturing prophecy of interplanetary travel. While it is true that this world with its one time huge distances has been in effect conquered, one must realize that that conquest cannot be fully claimed until the means of communication and travel have been placed within the reach of every one. This slow process of development necessarily involves intense and concentrated activity on the part of chemical industry which more than any other is charged with the duty of providing cheaply and in quantity the materials required to make what are now wonderful discoveries the commonplaces of every-day living.

267

MAN IN A CHEMICAL WORLD

The process of shrinking our world through inter-communication is being offset by even more important contributions of applied science to its enlarged productivity. Already has been mentioned the beneficent help of chemical products in increasing the available food supply to feed the growing hordes of men on the earth through greater productiveness of agriculture, preservation of the fruits of the earth for man's use and the conquest of territory now unavailable because of diseases yet untamed. The combination of these factors in making man's life more comfortable is having a pronounced effect in removing the causes of wars and international quarrels just as the free and prompt interchange of ideas is slowly but surely destroying those misunderstandings between men and nations upon which conflicts are built.

The future holds, through these things, a yet unrealized amity and fellowship, peace and good will among men, which as yet we can only envision dimly through clouds of misunderstanding that would threaten peace.

In industry, possession of what have been essential raw materials is ceasing to be of sufficient importance in this age of synthesis to cause strife. The nation unendowed by Nature with some hitherto invaluable natural resource need no longer want for it when the developments of synthetic chemistry provide ways of accomplishing the same thing with what is available. It is a matter of small consequence to the rider on a railroad train, whose sole object is to go from one place to another with comfort and dispatch, whether the rails upon which his conveyance travels are made of steel, or green cheese, or butterflies' wings so long as they adequately serve his purpose.

Cellulose, as the basis for the production of paper, has called upon the forests of the world to such a degree that serious question has arisen as to an adequate supply of the particular species of trees which have been found best adapted for the production of wood pulp. The resources of Canada, Norway, Sweden, Russia, and other countries have been drawn upon for the supply of the prodigious tonnage required for our daily papers alone. The question of growing annual crops for this purpose, or the utilization of such existing sources of supply as cornstalks, sugar cane and many other crops has met with economic as well as chemical difficulties. The problem seems to have been solved, however, by the use of what is known as the young slash or long leaf pine of the South. The general belief that the resin content of this particular species of pine would render it inapplicable for pulping purposes has been disproved by actual experiment. The pulping processes have been solved and this useful conifer which has hitherto been a chief source of what are commonly called "naval stores," that is, turpentine and rosin, as well as lumber, now promises to be an entirely new basis for wood pulp manufacture. Growing in a climate where the natural conditions for the development of cellulose in tree growth is at a maximum, this tree thrives from Texas to the Atlantic. It is said that within about a hundred miles of the Atlantic there are 18,000,000 acres available and this strip alone would be enough, because of the rapid growth of the young trees, to supply the necessary wood pulp now used by the entire country.

The place of chemistry in this investigation has been very important and in view of an increased use of cellulose in the industries, the solution of the problem seems to have been brought to fruition at the exact time when it is needed.

The modern development of other metals and alloys to supplement iron and steel in the service of man has quite definitely freed civilization from its abject dependence on these. So valuable are such new metals as aluminum, magnesium, chromium, molybdenum, nickel, beryllium, cadmium, and their alloys, that the iron and steel upon which the present phase of civilization has been built are already threatened and the day is not far distant when many of our iron implements will be treasured as mementos of a past age, just as stone implements are today.

In all human activities chemical industry is functioning and will continue to function by increasing the efficiency and effectiveness of man's labors. It is, of course, necessary to place the credit for the great strides forward that civilization has made at the feet of the great inventors, Edison, Morse, Bell, Fulton, Howe, Whitney, and others of their outstanding abilities, and to realize that the ultimate development of their ideas to the point where every human being can use them depends upon others. In other words, inspiration is but a part of the process by which comforts and conveniences are made available to us. Leonardo da Vinci invented a flying machine which might have flown successfully had his age been in possession of the experiences and materials at the command of the Wright Brothers centuries later. Without the many things that had been developed in the intervening period, the Wrights would have been no more successful than was da Vinci. In a very large measure, these essentials of materials and experience are available to us today and to our great inventors through the continuing activities of chemical industry. To realize the essential importance of materials to progress, one has but to compare the original flying machines of three decades ago with the swift air liners flying regularly over lands and oceans today; the telephone over which Bell first talked with today's easy and sure conversations over vast distances; the first incandescent electric lamp with modern lighting. In each of these cases, as in many others, the products of chemical industry peculiarly adapted to the purposes of the inventor have supplied the means by which his inspiration has been placed at the service of all men. In this way, chemical industry has contributed most importantly to our comforts and conveniences and will continue so to aid the gradual advance of our civilization.

The accepted measure of a civilization is the degree of its conquest of its environment, the ability of those making it up to control the forces of Nature and to adapt their operation to the service of man. By this materialistic gage of progress, chemical industry has become the most important single factor for it peculiarly controls and adapts the materials of Nature to man's needs. Today, the conquest of weather and the control of human feelings and abilities through what has become known as "air conditioning" presents a most interesting problem whose solution will undoubtedly be a crucial factor in human affairs in the next generation. Already, it is possible to believe that the necessary inventions have been made to give us precise control of weather within our dwellings and other buildings. That these are not now universally applied so that all may have comfort at all times is distinctly a problem in the use of materials. Perhaps the needed materials to perfect and to cheapen air conditioning to make it serviceable to all are already known and available, the ingenuity required to make them serve these purposes being the only factor lacking. On the other hand, there may lie just over the boundary of the future, startling discoveries of new materials which will hasten the coming of universal weather control.

In economic and industrial affairs, chemical industry is continuing to lighten men's burdens by multiplying the effectiveness of human labor. It is freeing human energies from drudgery and liberating human talents for leisure beyond the dreams of our forefathers. The impact of these advances in technology has been too great for our sociological abilities to bear for the time being and all manner of ills have risen to plague our enonomic structures. The progress of science and industry has been far more rapid during the past few decades than our ability to care for its consequences, and the unbalance of our economic and social structures resulting from the continual rapid-fire blows directed at them has encouraged every kind of dreamer to put forward untried or unsound cures for our economic ills. In these, there has been much that is false which must be carefully sifted out to leave the ultimate truths from which our future will be built. In a very real sense, economics and sociology have been taken unawares by problems with which they could not at the moment cope and a lapse of time and much serious labor will be required to bring these essentials of human happiness again into pace with the swiftly striding progress of technology.

Stop or handicap industrial research and we would at once elect ourselves the victims of the first foreign monopoly that chooses to exploit us. It is only about ten years ago that we paid $1.25 a pound for rubber, of which we use as much as the rest of the world combined, and import all of it. Thanks to industrial research, which developed a product superior to rubber out of coal, water, salt and limestone, America will never pay that price for rubber again. Dependence upon Germany for dyes and medicines and potash, upon Chile for nitrate, upon Trinidad for asphalt and Japan for camphor, has become independence only because America's industrial scientists fought for it and won.

Let us not deceive ourselves. The world trembles on the brink of changes that may make or unmake peoples. There are menaces of war, which, should it come, would disrupt orderly trade and force us to maintain ourselves apart. Foreshadowed is the increasingly rapid introduction of new goods, new materials and new methods, some of which will be revolutionary in effect. No longer can we be sure that the raw materials from which we made our goods yesterday will be the raw materials with which men will work tomorrow. Man has learned the secret of material creation and a new age impends.

Synthetic chemistry's hugely expanding possibilities have hardly been visioned yet. In the markets of the world less than 10,000 different individual chemical compounds are bought and sold as part of regular trade. Compared with this meager number, chemical literature records facts (often very incomplete) concerning a total of perhaps a hundred thousand more. In other words, we already know something about approximately ten times as many possible products of chemical industry as we now use. The numbers of potential synthetic chemicals of which we yet know nothing at all reach astronomical proportions very quickly as one applies the simple mathematics of probability to look into the future. In the single series of compounds of carbon with hydrogen of the type chemically known as paraffins which make up our natural gas and petroleum, a calculation shows that there are three million possible compounds made up of twenty carbon atoms and forty-two hydrogen atoms.

In the same series, compounds of twenty-six carbon atoms with fifty-four hydrogen atoms number more than 93 million and of those of thirty-one carbon atoms there are more than 10 billion. In another series of carbon and hydrogen compounds resembling acetylene, and chemically belonging to the acetylene series, those of twenty-five carbon atoms number more than 208 million and there are more than 27 billion containing thirty carbon atoms in each molecule. Similarly astounding figures are found for the numbers of possible alcohols belonging to the same series as grain alcohol. Of these there are 82 million containing twenty carbon atoms in the molecule, 712 million containing twenty-five, and nearly 96 billion containing thirty.

These figures indicate the possibilities among only the very simplest types of chemical compounds. As their complexity grows by the introduction of other kinds of atoms and different arrangements of atoms, the numbers of possibilities soar to unimaginable magnitudes. Yet each of these myriads of possibilities may be found invaluable for some human purpose and be some day synthesized for our use! When our knowledge is limited to hundreds of thousands and our industry to mere thousands of the billions of possibilities, we are certainly in no position to vision even darkly what may be realized by the next generation of chemical workers.

The return to the horse and buggy, the kerosene lamp, the stereopticon, and the ills and diseases of the days before automobiles, electric lights, motion pictures and modern sanitation would by no means solve our economic problems but would be the equivalent of suicide for our civilization. Rather than give way to such fatuous imaginings, men must goad their minds into producing new economic and sociological plans free from the shackles of the past as our material civilization has been liberated to allow us fully to enjoy the fruits of our own labors. To suggest what forms these new plans may take is quite beyond the scope of this discussion. One looks in vain among the thousand and one schemes which are daily failing to accomplish their announced purpose for one which stands out as offering the means of salvation. One has even greater difficulty, if possible, in finding among the great army of economic would-be Messiahs one possessing the strength of character and the vision to lead the way to the newer and brighter day provided for our race through the conquest of our material world. The many thoughts fermenting in men's minds today are destined ultimately by the slow processes of time to shape the structure of a new economy far better than any the race has known. The swift advance of technology has but for a moment run ahead of economics whose progress must, by its very nature, be gradual rather than revolutionary. Human opinions are stubborn and slow to change. Lacking this impediment, technology has outrun human nature's ability to adapt itself. Yet the evolutionary processes of the human mind are so stimulated by this material advance and by the instruments of mass education it has provided that one can state with certainty that the present and the succeeding generations will adapt themselves fully to the newer conditions. The result will be a better material and a better intellectual civilization than the world has yet seen.

We have examined, as thoroughly as so modest a volume will permit, the practical application of the chemical industry to our daily lives. We have found that from the first papyrus on which was recorded human thoughts, and the ink which made the record legi-

ble, all through history down to the innumerable publications which emanate from our modern presses,
chemical industry has played its important part. It has
recorded the achievement of the race and made available to all subsequent generations the knowledge gained
by our predecessors and the developing philosophy
and growing ethics of the past.

We have learned that the phonographic records
which record the masterpieces of music and the actual
voices of our great singers are children of chemical
industry. The complete revolution of our theatrical
amusements is due to the photographic film; the lamps
which give the light and the chemical developers which
give us not only the picture but the spoken word as well,
all are parts of chemical industry. We find also that the
radio, which will probably become the greatest educational force yet devised by man through which the
masses of people can be reached, would be impossible
without chemical industry.

We have spoken of transportation and have found
that the modern streamlined train and its source of
power, the airplane and the automobile are all chemical mechanisms. We have learned that our daily food
is made sanitary, safe, more nutritive and more complete in those vital elements which are necessary to life
itself because of chemical industry. Through chemical
industry, our water supply and the disposal of waste
have been made so safe that untold thousands of lives
are saved annually and we take it as a matter of course.
When our bodies are injured, antiseptics are ready to
save our lives, anesthetics to relieve the pain, and a

multitude of specially developed medicines aid the sick toward recovery.

Chemical industry furnishes the great industrial basis on which all other industries rest, and the strong arm of national security which will cause foreign nations to hesitate before attacking us. It furnishes a form of preparedness that makes for peace on a basis so sound that our country has no fear of war as long as our chemistry is developed and encouraged.

There is one great phase of civilization which is an outgrowth of the existence of the chemical industry which has not been touched upon and that is the contribution of our industry to intellectual development. One of the fundamentals laid down by our forefathers for the best preservation of our liberties was the theorem that every child should be educated to full capacity. It was believed, is still believed and is undoubtedly true, that any civilization which develops better education of the average man will develop in that nation an intelligence which will ultimately safeguard it no matter what theories or isms may develop to threaten the stability of its institutions.

Chemical industry makes available articles, substances, mechanisms, educational devices, new discoveries, new applications and develops new industries, spreading beneficially its influences far and wide, from the great outdoors to the kitchen. Chemistry makes audible the voices of our leaders, cheapens the cost of books, enables the public press to exist, furnishes the technical substances for research and, indeed, makes life safer, easier and better for all.

Chemistry is also building up in our country a civilization of a type so high that it must automatically have its effect for the betterment and national advance not only of the human being physically, which is now made so eloquently evident by the extension of the life span which has taken place in the last few decades, but also of the human mind spiritually by freeing man from fear of hunger for creature necessities. It has added to his leisure and broadened his interests and will add to the reasoning power and broader common sense of every individual whose better conditions become apparent to him. Chemical industry, by making life easier and safer, is freeing man for the cultivation of the arts and graces of life upon which the future philosophies of life will depend.

Dreams of the present lead to most extraordinary results in the coming years. Cosmic rays are now in the forefront of intensive investigation. What purpose do they now serve, what effects may they produce, and to what useful end may they be diverted? The bombardment of the atom by powerful electric charges has already turned platinum to gold. Theoretically, transmutation is at hand. With these early beginnings already developed, will a method of producing these changes economically be found, and if so will all our standards of money and economics be upset because man can produce the rarest metals at will? An expectation of such a result is not more visionary than to have supposed that the Hertzian waves would ever give us the radio and television.

Will man succeed in breaking the atom and releasing

its energy so that it can be utilized for power? Today
this is not probable, and the energy required to break
the atom is believed to be greater than that produced.
Will the investigations of the future finally disclose the
ultimate source of energy that forms the atom and
bring to the mind of man the knowledge of how to
unlock this mystery? Will the gap in our knowledge
as to the true source of the energy in the sun finally
disclose that it is "intra-atomic energy released under
the conditions of temperature and pressure within the
sun?" One still hesitates to acknowledge it because
of the enormous difficulties involved. But does there
not lie within the solution of this problem of the mysterious continuous emission of enormous energy through
billions of years the key which will unlock many doors
of practical utility? Within the last generation many
of the elements which had been regarded as mere curi-
osities have come into fields of great usefulness and
many others of which we now know little may serve
purposes at present utterly undreamed of.

Shall we discover what gives a magnet its permanent
power? Shall we learn what orients the molecules and
brings about surface tension in a drop of water or
mercury? When will we learn the mysteries of adsorp-
tion and why the molecules of gas pile one upon another in activated charcoal and be able to give this
property to other substances disclosing further applications at present unsuspected? Will we learn what makes
matter attract all other matter at a distance? What is
gravity, how fast does gravity travel, can it be neutral-
ized? Will the philosophy of the world be changed

again by new discoveries here and the aviator find himself outfitted with no wings at all?

In this year 1937, we can point with pride to past achievements but verily the future holds possibilities so far beyond our dreams that we must admit that we have just opened the door through which our successors will be admitted to a new realm of discovery far greater than we can imagine.

Drawing its sustenance from the findings of earnest workers in pure science and engineering, chemical industry bears worthily a burden of responsibility to the whole people in translating scientific abstractions into the materials of everyday life. Its collective responsibility is shared among many persons, each of whom must assume a proper part. Fortunate indeed is this industry in its ability to select and train individuals of the highest types for its service. Upon them collectively and individually rests responsibility not alone to their immediate superiors for the activities in which each is engaged but more importantly to the world at large and to the great armies of workers in other industries whose livelihoods essentially depend on the products of their labors. A realization of this responsibility extends throughout the industry from the lowliest laborer to the controller of the destinies of large enterprises and to the lives of each it gives a purposefulness seldom found in other walks of life.

There is great satisfaction to all those engaged in the chemical industry when they realize that no matter how humble their connection with it, they have the opportunity to do their part in developing an activity

which means so much to the world at large. Many occupations in this world, while profitable, make no contribution to human advancement. Employment in such
occupations may be satisfactory to the unthinking, but
whoever realizes that employment in the chemical industry is an opportunity to serve in a fundamental occupation, upon which all others rest, without which our
country would become a backward nation, and out of
which grows civilization itself, glows with justifiable
pride in the fact that his life has purpose and that he
is serving humanity well. He, individually, feels that he
is making a contribution to the industrial and intellectual development of all people everywhere, and especially to our country, the greatest nation in the world.

L'Envoi

THE glimpses of chemical industry's service to man afforded by this book could be presented only by utilizing innumerable chemical products. The first outline of its plan began to take shape on chemically produced notepaper with the aid of a piece of chemically-treated graphite held in a synthetic resin pencil. Early corrections were made with erasers of chemically compounded rubber. In its ultimate haven on the shelves of your bookcase, it will rest on a coating of chemical varnish behind a pane of chemically produced glass. Nowhere has it been separated from that industry's products.

The manuscript was typed on a modern typewriter composed principally of metallic alloys. Pressure on its keys of synthetic resin forced alloy type faces against a textile ribbon which left impressions in synthetic dye on paper supported by a chemically compounded rubber roller. Later, the entire typescript was reproduced in manifold through the chemical process of photolithography for review by many persons.

Ultimately, the type from which the book was printed was cast in alloy metal, corrected and finally electrotyped by a process involving numerous other chemical products and reactions. Impressions from this type were made with ink consisting of carbon black (recovered from natural gas) in a varnish chemically prepared. The ink was spread upon the type by rolls of gelatin chemically compounded with glycerine and transferred to paper chemically made from spruce trees.

The artists prepared drawings with inks of a different character, but of similar chemical origin, and these originals were reproduced by photochemical engraving to form plates adapted to the purposes of the printer.

The printed sheets, after assembly, were stitched with chemically treated thread, glued with chemical adhesives and bound between pulp boards, chemical products of the forest, decorated and protected by cloth heavily sized with a chemical mixture.

So, with a final appreciation for your courtesy in accompanying us on this excursion through chemical industry, we bid you adieu.

THE AUTHOR.

Index

287

INDEX

INDEX

INDEX

INDEX

Quartz, 4, 221
Quartz, Fused, 55
Quick-freezing, 200
Quinine, 64, 65

Radio, 146
Rags, 134
Railroads, 105, 198
Rain, 6
Rare gases, 21, 197, 225
Rats, 48
Rayon, 18, 137, 160, 172, 232, 247
Red lead, 183
Refrigeration, 78, 95, 200, 225
Resins, Natural, 98, 152, 180, 181
Resins, Synthetic, 26, 98, 125, 142, 152, 184, 228
Roads, 101, 108
Rochelle salt, 156
Rosin, 98, 136, 152, 269
Rotenone, 89
Rubber, 96, 98, 108, 111, 146, 151, 227, 257, 273
Rubber, Synthetic, 231
Ruby, 219, 259
Rust, see Corrosion

Safety paper, 138
Salt, 21, 22, 46, 79, 82, 86, 108, 166, 219
Salt cake, 193
Saltpeter, 71, 77, 273
Salvarsan, 47, 65
Sand, 85, 192, 193, 219
Sanitary ware, 198
Sapphire, 219, 259
Sawdust, 219
Sea water, see Brine
Selenium, 157
Serums, 49, 94, 236
Sewage, 41, 42
Shellac, 98, 152
Shingles, 178
Ships, 130
"Silcrome," 123
Silica, 4, 85
Silicates, 163
Silicon, 4, 5, 103, 157
Silicon carbide, 219
Silk, 14, 16, 160, 171, 173
Silk, Artificial, see Rayon
Silk, Weighting, 171
Silver, 3, 123, 157
Small-pox, 48
Smelting, 102
Smoke screens, 83, 234
Smokeless powder, 185
Soap, 42, 161, 164, 165, 199, 246
Soda, 108, 135, 162
Soda ash, 193
Soda, Baking, 239
Sodium, 55, 129 .

Sodium bicarbonate, 239
Sodium bichromate, 27
Sodium metaphosphate, 209
Sodium nitrate, 207
Sodium orthosilicate, 163
Sodium silicate, 98, 163
Soil, 69
Solder, 96
Solvents, 28, 97, 201, 228, 239
Soot, see Carbon black
Soy beans, 28, 98
Spectroscope, 5
Spinnerets, 173
Spinning, 160
Stainless steel, 131
Starch, 97, 98, 187
Stars, 5
Steam, 208, 211
Steel, 102, 103, 104, 106, 119, 121, 124, 131, 156, 183, 207, 209, 210
Stone, Artificial, 24
Storage battery, 127
Strontium, 148
Stucco, 178, 179
Sugar, 96
Sulfate process, 136
Sulfite process, 135
Sulfur, 21, 55, 86, 88, 111, 228
Sulfur dioxide, 46, 95, 96, 135, 166
Sulfuric acid, 22, 83, 86, 92, 96, 116, 127, 137, 161, 163, 173, 185, 206, 207, 212, 228, 239
Sulfuric ether, see Ether
Sun, 5
Superphosphate, 84, 86
Synthesis, 7, 12, 25, 54, 63, 97, 259, 263, 266, 274

Tank-cars, 78
Tannic acid, 138
Tanning, 176
Tantalum, 196, 222
Tars, 108, 181. See also Coal tar
Tear gases, 237, 238
Telegraph, 143
Telephone, 145
Television, 157
Tellurium, 117
Tetra-ethyl lead, 117
Textiles, 159, 164, 229, 244
Thorium, 148
Thymol, 60
Thyroxin, 66
Tiles, 178
Tin, 96, 171, 183, 231
Tires, 106, 108, 110, 128
Titanium, 103, 220
Titanium carbide, 220
Titanium white, 182, 188
T. N. T., 169
Tools, 124, 220
Trade wastes, 44

INDEX